curriculum mathematics practice **2**

C Oliver   **A Ledsham**   **R Elvin**   **M Bindley**

Oxford University Press

OXFORD
UNIVERSITY PRESS

Great Clarendon Street, Oxford OX2 6DP

Oxford University Press is a department of the University of Oxford.
It furthers the University's objective of excellence in research,
scholarship, and education by publishing worldwide in

Oxford New York

Auckland Cape Town Dar es Salaam Hong Kong Karachi
Kuala Lumpur Madrid Melbourne Mexico City Nairobi
New Delhi Shanghai Taipei Toronto

With offices in

Argentina Austria Brazil Chile Czech Republic France Greece
Guatemala Hungary Italy Japan Poland Portugal Singapore
South Korea Switzerland Thailand Turkey Ukraine Vietnam

Oxford is a registered trade mark of Oxford University Press
in the UK and in certain other countries

Series first published as *Comprehensive Mathematics Practice* 1981
Updated edition of *Curriculum Mathematics Practice* first published 1996
10

ISBN 13 978 0 19 833742 3
ISBN 0 19 833742 6
A CIP record for this book is available from the British Library.

Typeset and illustrated by Tech-Set Ltd
Printed and bound in Great Britain by Bell & Bain Ltd, Glasgow

Mixed Sources
Product group from well-managed
forests and other controlled sources
www.fsc.org Cert no. TT-COC-002769
© 1996 Forest Stewardship Council

Preface

Curriculum Mathematics Practice is an updated version of *Comprehensive Mathematics Practice*, a successful series designed for the majority of students in their first years of secondary schooling. As before, the books provide a vast range of carefully constructed and graded exercises in a coherent mathematical progression, with many of these exercises set in a real-life context. The levels targeted are 3–8, and details of how all six new books relate to the curriculum are given in the Answer Book.

These new books do not attempt to provide a complete scheme for the National Curriculum. No attempt has been made for instance to cover 'Using and Applying Mathematics' or computer work. It is expected, however, that mathematics departments will use other resources for those aspects (e.g. *Oxford Mathematics*) and that *Curriculum Mathematics Practice* will provide a core of skill practice within an overall scheme of work.

The series has the same objective as the original books. The series should enable students 'to gain confidence in their abilities and master the fundamental processes so necessary for future success'.

Mark Bindley
Revising Editor
December 1995

Contents

Unit 1 Decimal place value

Decimal place value

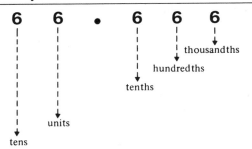

The number shown is made up of 6 tens, 6 units, 6 tenths, 6 hundredths, and 6 thousandths.
The number is read as 'sixty-six point six six six'.
Note the decimal point which separates whole numbers from fractions.
Once again, the value of each digit depends upon its place value.

Example 1

Give the value of each underlined figure.

a 4.<u>3</u>2   **b** 10.4<u>7</u>   **c** 1.02<u>4</u>

a Three-tenths or $\frac{3}{10}$ or 0.3

b Seven-hundredths or $\frac{7}{100}$ or 0.07

c Four-thousandths or $\frac{4}{1000}$ or 0.004

Exercise 1.1

Give the value of each underlined figure.

1 3.<u>5</u>4	**2** 8.<u>2</u>3	**3** 5.3<u>7</u>	**4** 2.1<u>9</u>
5 10.5<u>2</u>	**6** 4.0<u>5</u>	**7** 7.0<u>6</u>	**8** 5.<u>4</u>
9 6.<u>1</u>	**10** 3.6<u>5</u>2	**11** 5.8<u>4</u>7	**12** 1.<u>2</u>33
13 5.2<u>5</u>2	**14** 4.6<u>7</u>1	**15** 7.31<u>5</u>	**16** 2.53<u>6</u>
17 1.84<u>5</u>	**18** 6.32<u>2</u>	**19** 5.0<u>3</u>5	**20** 8.0<u>4</u>4
21 9.05<u>6</u>	**22** 4.01<u>7</u>	**23** 5.30<u>4</u>	**24** 2.00<u>6</u>
25 7.00<u>3</u>			

Example 2

Arrange the following numbers in order of size, starting with the smallest.

a 4.04, 40.4, 0.404, 404

The order is: 0.404, 4.04, 40.4, 404

b 6, 6.006, 6.6, 6.016, 6.06

The order is: 6, 6.006, 6.016, 6.06, 6.6

Exercise 1.2

Arrange the numbers in each question in order of size, starting with the smallest.

1 5.02, 5.22, 5, 5.2
2 4.33, 4, 4.03, 4.3
3 7.04, 7.4, 7.004, 7.44, 7.044, 7
4 8.005, 8.55, 8.5, 8.055, 8, 8.05
5 3.11, 3, 3.1, 3.01, 3.011, 3.001
6 5.03, 5.33, 0.53, 5.3
7 7.2, 7.22, 7.02, 0.72
8 6.05, 0.65, 6.55, 6.5
9 3.024, 0.324, 3.24, 32.4, 3.204
10 5.061, 56.1, 5.601, 0.561, 5.61
11 4.803, 0.483, 4.083, 4.83, 48.3, 48.03
12 2.705, 27.5, 2.75, 0.275, 2.075, 27.05

Example 3

Give the smallest number and the largest number that can be made using *all* the following digits and a decimal point.

a 3, 7, 4, 1   **b** 4, 0, 7   **c** 2, 0, 0, 2

a The smallest number is 1.347, the largest number is 743.1.

b The smallest number is 0.47, the largest number is 74.0.

c The smallest number is 0.022, the largest number is 220.0.

Note A whole number is written 740, or 740.0; never write 740. for this number.
A decimal fraction is written 0.47 but never .47.

Exercise 1.3

For each question give the smallest number and the largest number that can be made using *all* the digits and a decimal point.

1 3, 5, 6	**2** 4, 1, 8	**3** 9, 2, 3
4 7, 5, 4	**5** 2, 0, 5	**6** 6, 0, 7
7 2, 5, 3, 1	**8** 4, 6, 5, 7	**9** 8, 9, 4, 3
10 3, 6, 1, 5	**11** 7, 2, 8, 4	**12** 3, 0, 5, 2
13 1, 0, 7, 8	**14** 3, 0, 0, 4	**15** 7, 0, 0, 9

To multiply a number by 10, you should move each figure one place to the left. To multiply a number by 100, move each figure two places to the left.

This rule is also followed when multiplying decimals.

Example 4

Work out the following.

a 4.6×10 **b** 1.1×100 **c** 0.23×10
d 0.05×10 **e** 0.004×100

a $4.6 \times 10 = 46.0$
   U.t   TU.t

b $1.1 \times 100 = 110$
   U.t   HTU.t

c $0.23 \times 10 = 2.3$

d $0.05 \times 10 = 0.5$

e $0.004 \times 100 = 0.4$

Exercise 1.4

Multiply each of the following by 10.

1 3.25	**2** 5.36	**3** 1.84	**4** 4.05
5 2.08	**6** 5.4	**7** 8.2	**8** 9.1
9 0.26	**10** 0.57	**11** 0.89	**12** 0.3
13 0.9	**14** 0.1	**15** 0.03	**16** 0.07
17 0.425	**18** 0.641	**19** 0.118	**20** 0.402
21 0.105	**22** 0.004	**23** 0.009	**24** 0.054
25 0.017			

Multiply each of the following by 100.

26 0.453	**27** 0.627	**28** 0.121	**29** 0.508
30 0.906	**31** 0.064	**32** 0.038	**33** 0.005
34 0.002	**35** 0.36	**36** 0.92	**37** 0.55
38 0.04	**39** 0.09	**40** 0.3	**41** 0.8
42 0.1	**43** 5.27	**44** 3.94	**45** 1.22
46 2.03	**47** 6.06	**48** 5.2	**49** 3.9
50 1.1			

To divide a number by 10, move all the figures one place to the right.
To divide a number by 100, move all the figures two places to the right.

Example 5

Work out the following.

a $6.4 \div 10$ **b** $6 \div 10$ **c** $7.3 \div 100$
d $0.4 \div 100$

a $6.4 \div 10 = 0.64$
   U.t   U.th

b $6 \div 10 = 0.6$
   U   U.t

c $7.3 \div 100 = 0.073$

d $0.4 \div 100 = 0.004$

Exercise 1.5

Divide each of the following by 10.

1 5.6	**2** 3.2	**3** 9.7	**4** 4.35
5 1.58	**6** 2.16	**7** 3.09	**8** 5
9 8	**10** 2	**11** 25.4	**12** 67.1
13 95.7	**14** 50.6	**15** 32	**16** 75
17 99	**18** 0.19	**19** 0.83	**20** 0.55
21 0.3	**22** 0.7	**23** 0.1	**24** 0.05
25 0.02			

Divide each of the following by 100.

26 35.2	**27** 81.6	**28** 40.5	**29** 20.1
30 37	**31** 62	**32** 50	**33** 125
34 236	**35** 5.34	**36** 9.95	**37** 4.74
38 1.08	**39** 5.8	**40** 3.6	**41** 1.5
42 0.27	**43** 0.61	**44** 0.32	**45** 0.05
46 0.08	**47** 0.04	**48** 0.8	**49** 0.3
50 0.1			

Exercise 1.6

Copy the following and fill in the empty spaces.

1 $2.6 \times 10 =$	**2** $ \times 10 = 26$
3 $2.6 \times = 26$	**4** $3.25 \times 10 =$
5 $ \times 10 = 32.5$	**6** $3.25 \times = 32.5$
7 $5.42 \times 100 =$	**8** $ \times 100 = 542$
9 $5.42 \times = 542$	**10** $4.8 \times 100 =$
11 $ \times 100 = 480$	**12** $4.8 \times = 480$
13 $18.6 \div 10 =$	**14** $ \div 10 = 1.86$
15 $18.6 \div = 1.86$	**16** $3.41 \div 10 =$
17 $ \div 10 = 0.341$	**18** $3.41 \div = 0.341$
19 $61.5 \div 100 =$	**20** $ \div 100 = 0.615$

To multiply a number by 1000, move all the figures three places to the left.
To divide a number by 1000, move all the figures three places to the right.

Example 6

Work out the following.

a 3.4×1000 **b** 78×1000
c 213.0456×1000 **d** $3.4 \div 1000$
e $78 \div 1000$ **f** $213.0456 \div 1000$

a $3.4 \times 1000 = 3400$

b $78 \times 1000 = 78\,000$

c $213.0456 \times 1000 = 213\,045.6$

d $3.4 \div 1000 = 0.0034$

e $78 \div 1000 = 0.078$

f $213.0456 \div 1000 = 0.213\,045\,6$

Exercise 1.7

Multiply each of the following by 1000.

1 34.56	**2** 2.45	**3** 13
4 0.13	**5** 1.6	**6** 5.9
7 6.3	**8** 3.66	**9** 0.056
10 0.001	**11** 0.1	**12** 123
13 0.123	**14** 12.3	**15** 1.23
16 0.0123	**17** 683.34	**18** 0.001 23
19 6.8334	**20** 6833.4	**21** 68 334
22 0.683 34	**23** 0.000 001	**24** 45.99
25 500.005		

Divide each of the following by 1000.

26 678	**27** 67.8	**28** 6.78
29 0.678	**30** 0.0678	**31** 4000
32 400	**33** 40	**34** 4
35 0.4	**36** 0.04	**37** 0.004
38 55 555	**39** 5555.5	**40** 555.55
41 55.555	**42** 5.5555	**43** 0.555 55
44 34.67	**45** 60.04	**46** 12 789
47 45.01	**48** 7	**49** 0.0007
50 1000		

Example 7

a Write 345 as another number multiplied by 1000.
b Write 345 as another number divided by 1000.

a $345 = 0.345 \times 1000$

b $345 = 345\,000 \div 1000$

Exercise 1.8

Write each of these numbers as another number multiplied by 1000.

1 20 000	**2** 2000	**3** 200
4 20	**5** 2	**6** 0.2
7 0.02	**8** 0.002	**9** 0.0002
10 756	**11** 2908	**12** 34.26
13 0.5	**14** 5000	**15** 67.9
16 8904.5	**17** 25 000	**18** 0.855
19 1	**20** 0.017	

Write each of these numbers as another number divided by 1000.

21 50 000	**22** 5000	**23** 500
24 50	**25** 5	**26** 0.5
27 0.05	**28** 0.005	**29** 0.0005
30 23	**31** 0.23	**32** 4.007
33 12.4	**34** 1.24	**35** 124
36 0.001	**37** 0.0001	**38** 1000
39 1	**40** 3.142	

Adding and subtracting

To add decimal fractions, put the decimal points underneath each other to make sure that each figure is in its proper place.

Example 8

Add to find the 'odd answer out'.

a $0.4 + 0.5 + 0.6$ **b** $0.2 + 0.7 + 0.6$
c $0.9 + 0.7 + 0.9$ **d** $0.8 + 0.2 + 0.5$

a		**b**		**c**		**d**	
	0.4		0.2		0.9		0.8
	0.5		0.7		0.7		0.2
	+0.6		+0.6		+0.9		+0.5
	1.5		1.5		2.5		1.5

So **c** is the 'odd answer out'.

Exercise 1.9

Add to find the 'odd answer out'.

1
  a $0.2 + 0.7 + 0.4$
  b $0.6 + 0.1 + 0.8$
  c $0.3 + 0.2 + 0.8$
  d $0.7 + 0.3 + 0.3$

2
  a $0.6 + 0.8 + 0.4$
  b $0.5 + 0.9 + 0.2$
  c $0.4 + 0.5 + 0.7$
  d $0.3 + 0.8 + 0.5$

3
  a $0.9 + 0.8 + 0.6$
  b $0.6 + 0.5 + 1.2$
  c $1.2 + 0.7 + 0.4$
  d $0.6 + 0.8 + 0.7$

4
  a $0.9 + 0.7 + 0.8$
  b $0.2 + 0.5 + 1.5$
  c $1.3 + 0.4 + 0.7$
  d $1.1 + 1.2 + 0.1$

5
  a $1.3 + 0.5 + 0.8$
  b $0.4 + 1.7 + 0.5$
  c $1.2 + 1.4 + 0.2$
  d $0.9 + 0.9 + 0.8$

6
  a $1.4 + 1.5 + 0.3$
  b $0.2 + 1.7 + 1.5$
  c $1.7 + 0.9 + 0.6$
  d $0.5 + 1.8 + 0.9$

7
  a $1.5 + 1.3 + 1.8$
  b $2.8 + 0.6 + 1.4$
  c $3.8 + 0.7 + 0.3$
  d $2.2 + 2.5 + 0.1$

8
  a $2.8 + 1.9 + 0.8$
  b $2.5 + 2.8 + 0.4$
  c $1.5 + 0.9 + 3.3$
  d $2.2 + 1.4 + 2.1$

9
  a $2.5 + 2.3 + 1.6$
  b $3.2 + 1.5 + 1.7$
  c $1.8 + 0.7 + 3.9$
  d $2.8 + 0.9 + 2.9$

10
  a $5.8 + 1.4 + 1.9$
  b $2.7 + 3.8 + 2.6$
  c $4.2 + 3.5 + 1.6$
  d $5.1 + 3.4 + 0.6$

Example 9

Add to find the 'odd answer out'.

a $3.46 + 1.2\ \ + 5.36$
b $3.34 + 4\ \ \ \ + 2.78$ (hint: write 4 as 4.0)
c $2.14 + 5.08 + 2.9$

$$
\begin{array}{ccc}
\textbf{a} \quad 3.46 & \textbf{b} \quad 3.34 & \textbf{c} \quad 2.14 \\
1.2 & 4.0 & 5.08 \\
+\,5.36 & +\,2.78 & +\,2.9 \\
\hline
10.02 & 10.12 & 10.12 \\
\end{array}
$$

So **a** is the 'odd answer out'.

Exercise 1.10

Add to find the 'odd answer out'.

1
  a $2.13 + 4.37 + 3.12$
  b $2.65 + 4.21 + 2.56$
  c $5.81 + 2.37 + 1.44$

2
  a $2.28 + 2.16 + 3.4$
  b $4.29 + 1.3 + 2.15$
  c $3.9 + 2.31 + 1.53$

3
  a $2.63 + 1.4 + 2.5$
  b $2.1 + 3.38 + 1.15$
  c $2.89 + 0.24 + 3.5$

4
  a $5.82 + 3.31 + 1.33$
  b $4.92 + 3.14 + 2.4$
  c $6.56 + 1.7 + 2.3$

5
  a $5.49 + 2.8 + 2.46$
  b $4.93 + 3.09 + 2.75$
  c $5.97 + 1.78 + 3$

6
  a $3.53 + 4.14 + 1.39$
  b $2.21 + 5.12 + 1.75$
  c $5.46 + 3.02 + 0.6$

7
  a $8.43 + 4.07 + 2.82$
  b $5.78 + 3.44 + 6.2$
  c $2.09 + 4.33 + 9$

8
  a $7.62 + 3.24 + 1.64$
  b $5.19 + 3.06 + 4.25$
  c $3.97 + 5.57 + 2.76$

9
  a $5.65 + 0.81 + 2.44$
  b $4.73 + 1.02 + 2.34$
  c $2.53 + 5.2 + 1.17$

10
  a $5.41 + 4.32 + 1.27$
  b $4.6 + 5.16 + 2.24$
  c $3.92 + 4.6 + 3.48$

11
  a $6.5 + 9.84 + 3.66$
  b $9.57 + 4.43 + 7$
  c $8.91 + 5.03 + 6.06$

12
  a $12.48 + 11.37 + 1.15$
  b $11.01 + 10.65 + 2.34$
  c $12.08 + 11.3 + 1.62$

13
  a $11.24 + 10.31 + 13.45$
  b $11.52 + 12.36 + 12.12$
  c $13.2 + 12.67 + 10.13$

14
  a $13.02 + 5.52 + 11.46$
  b $18.31 + 4.54 + 6.15$
  c $19.22 + 4.4 + 6.38$

15
  a $15.24 + 12.3 + 14.46$
  b $13.12 + 11.6 + 15.28$
  c $14.87 + 13.13 + 12$

16
  a $13.85 + 15.15 + 15$
  b $15.92 + 17.08 + 12$
  c $10.3 + 21.16 + 12.54$

17
  a $14.25 + 11.1 + 1.65$
  b $11.38 + 12 + 3.62$
  c $12.19 + 3 + 10.81$

18
  a $13.07 + 15.5 + 1.43$
  b $11.35 + 4 + 14.65$
  c $15.79 + 13 + 2.21$

To subtract decimal fractions, once again make sure that the figures are in their right places by putting the decimal points underneath each other.

Example 10

Subtract to find the 'odd answer out'.

a $2.6 - 1.4$
b $2.4 - 1.2$
c $3.7 - 2.5$
d $9.6 - 8.5$

$$
\begin{array}{cccc}
\textbf{a} \quad 2.6 & \textbf{b} \quad 2.4 & \textbf{c} \quad 3.7 & \textbf{d} \quad 9.6 \\
-\,1.4 & -\,1.2 & -\,2.5 & -\,8.5 \\
\hline
1.2 & 1.2 & 1.2 & 1.1 \\
\end{array}
$$

So **d** is the 'odd answer out'.

Example 11

Subtract to find the 'odd answer out'.

a $4 - 2.6$ (write 4 as 4.0)
b $5.2 - 2.8$
c $9 - 6.6$ (write 9 as 9.0)
d $6.6 - 4.2$

a	4.0	**b**	5.2	**c**	9.0	**d**	6.6
	− 2.6		− 2.8		− 6.6		− 4.2
	1.4		2.4		2.4		2.4

So **a** is the 'odd answer out'.

Example 12

Subtract to find the difference between the following pairs of numbers and so find the 'odd answer out'.

a 7.5 and 1.26   (write 7.5 as 7.50)
b 34 and 27.66   (write 34 as 34.00)
c 10.63 and 4.39

a	7.50	**b**	34.00	**c**	10.63
	− 1.26		− 27.66		− 4.39
	6.24		6.34		6.24

So **b** is the 'odd answer out'.

Exercise 1.11

Subtract to find the 'odd answer out'.

1 a $3.9 - 2.3$
 b $6.6 - 5.2$
 c $5.5 - 4.1$
 d $2.8 - 1.4$

2 a $5.9 - 3.6$
 b $4.8 - 2.3$
 c $7.5 - 5.2$
 d $6.4 - 4.1$

3 a $5.6 - 3.4$
 b $8.9 - 6.5$
 c $9.3 - 7.1$
 d $3.5 - 1.3$

4 a $4.8 - 1.5$
 b $7.6 - 4.3$
 c $6.5 - 3.2$
 d $9.7 - 6.6$

5 a $7.8 - 3.3$
 b $5.9 - 1.4$
 c $8.7 - 4.1$
 d $6.5 - 2$

6 a $9.9 - 6.5$
 b $5.6 - 2.2$
 c $8.4 - 5$
 d $6.8 - 3.3$

7 a $6.9 - 1.8$
 b $8.7 - 3.5$
 c $9.6 - 4.4$
 d $7.8 - 2.6$

8 a $8.5 - 2.2$
 b $7.6 - 1.4$
 c $9.3 - 3.1$
 d $6.9 - 0.7$

9 a $6.9 - 1.4$
 b $7.8 - 2.3$
 c $9.7 - 4.1$
 d $8.5 - 3$

10 a $9.6 - 3.2$
 b $7.8 - 1.3$
 c $6.9 - 0.5$
 d $8.5 - 2.1$

11 a $4.4 - 1.8$
 b $6.5 - 3.9$
 c $7.1 - 4.5$
 d $5.2 - 2.7$

12 a $7.4 - 5.6$
 b $8.5 - 6.8$
 c $3.2 - 1.5$
 d $5.6 - 3.9$

13 a $5.2 - 2.3$
 b $7.5 - 4.6$
 c $6.6 - 3.8$
 d $8.3 - 5.4$

14 a $6.2 - 2.6$
 b $5.5 - 1.8$
 c $8.3 - 4.7$
 d $7.1 - 3.5$

15 a $8.2 - 3.4$
 b $6.5 - 1.7$
 c $7.4 - 2.6$
 d $9.7 - 4.8$

16 a $8.3 - 2.7$
 b $7.2 - 1.5$
 c $9.5 - 3.8$
 d $6.6 - 0.9$

17 a $9.3 - 4.5$
 b $6.6 - 1.8$
 c $8.4 - 3.7$
 d $5.2 - 0.4$

18 a $5.3 - 2.8$
 b $6.4 - 3.9$
 c $4.1 - 1.7$
 d $7 - 4.5$

19 a $8.5 - 4.9$
 b $5.4 - 1.8$
 c $4.3 - 0.7$
 d $9 - 5.6$

20 a $7.5 - 1.8$
 b $9.3 - 3.7$
 c $8.1 - 2.5$
 d $6 - 0.4$

Exercise 1.12

Subtract to find the difference between the following pairs of numbers and so find the 'odd answer out'.

1 a 8.59 and 3.25
 b 6.62 and 1.38
 c 9.23 and 3.89

2 a 9.39 and 4.83
 b 5.73 and 1.27
 c 8.14 and 3.68

3 a 8.32 and 2.87
 b 9.04 and 3.49
 c 7.07 and 1.52

4 a 6.58 and 0.23
 b 8.36 and 2.01
 c 9.27 and 3.02

5 a 5.49 and 0.86
 b 5.17 and 0.64
 c 9.62 and 5.09

6 a 7.95 and 4.5
 b 5.35 and 1.8
 c 9.15 and 5.6

7 a 7.27 and 2.9
 b 4.87 and 0.4
 c 5.17 and 0.8

8 a 9.7 and 4.28
 b 6.8 and 1.19
 c 8.2 and 2.78

9 a 5.2 and 1.66
 b 8 and 4.46
 c 6.7 and 3.06

10 a 6.8 and 2.08
 b 4.81 and 0.09
 c 4.6 and 0.08

11 a 46.97 and 36.45
 b 28.18 and 17.93
 c 14.02 and 3.77

12 a 60.87 and 38.82
 b 44.5 and 19.48
 c 28.6 and 6.55

13 a 22.63 and 7.49
 b 38.06 and 22.92
 c 42.91 and 28.76

14 a 30.3 and 9.28
 b 23.02 and 2.9
 c 43.11 and 22.99

15 a 32.09 and 23.53
 b 20.73 and 12.08
 c 16 and 7.44

Example 13

Find the 'odd answer out'.

a £1.63 + £2.07 + £3.49
b £10.93 − £2.74
c £20 − £12.81

a	£	**b**	£	**c**	£
	1.63		10.93		20.00
	2.07	−	2.74	−	12.81
+	3.49		8.19		7.19
	7.19				

So **b** is the 'odd answer out'.

Exercise 1.13

Find the 'odd answer out'.

1 **a** £3.44 + £4.23 + £3.31
  b £4.25 + £5.39 + £1.14
  c £4.67 + £2.78 + £3.53

2 **a** £12.52 + £21.14 + £11.34
  b £18.26 + £12.41 + £13.33
  c £16.34 + £17.20 + £11.46

3 **a** £16.58 + £22.30 + £11.12
  b £32.03 + £14.57 + £13.40
  c £22.71 + £12.29 + £25

4 **a** £12.10 + £10.75 + £2.15
  b £11.38 + £11.15 + £2.47
  c £13.80 + £2.76 + £7.44

5 **a** £4.13 + £8.47 + £2.52
  b £10.10 + £1.40 + £0.65
  c £6.62 + £3.50 + £5

6 **a** £56.89 − £13.65
  b £61.92 − £19.58
  c £59.11 − £16.77

7 **a** £43.20 − £18.68
  b £51.32 − £25.90
  c £75.02 − £49.60

8 **a** £31.70 − £13.54
  b £34 − £15.84
  c £30.08 − £13.90

9 **a** £19.85 − £3.34
  b £18.47 − £2.86
  c £19.30 − £2.79

10 **a** £12.68 − £8.12
  b £11.29 − £6.83
  c £10.25 − £5.79

11 **a** £15.36 + £13.47 + £12.32
  b £17.09 + £20.41 + £13.64
  c £54.78 − £13.63

12 **a** £15.80 + £10.30 + £6.26
  b £19.05 + £7.30 + £6.01
  c £51.82 − £18.56

13 **a** £11.96 + £5.58 + £9
  b £9.70 + £7.39 + £8.55
  c £29.53 − £3.89

14 **a** £10.52 + £3.15 + £1.76
  b £11 + £2.69 + £0.84
  c £22.71 − £7.28

15 **a** £8 + £6.46 + £5.36
  b £13.97 + £4.60 + £0.35
  c £25.20 − £5.38

16 **a** £3.53 + £4.48 + £1.74
  b £24.78 − £15.13
  c £22.84 − £13.19

17 **a** £2.51 + £3.75 + £2.38
  b £32.49 − £23.85
  c £13.42 − £4.88

18 **a** £4 + £0.60 + £3.85
  b £9.19 − £0.64
  c £9.20 − £0.75

19 **a** £0.95 + £0.76 + £7.82
  b £10.45 − £0.82
  c £11 − £1.37

20 **a** £20 + £16.26 + £3.79
  b £52.40 − £12.35
  c £52 − £1.96

Exercise 1.14

1 Find the length of the spade.

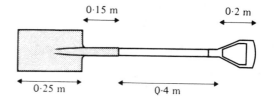

2 Find the
height of
the clock
tower.

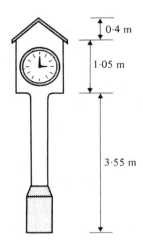

0·4 m

1·05 m

3·55 m

3

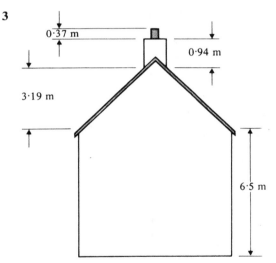

0·37 m

0·94 m

3·19 m

6·5 m

Find the height of the chimney top above the ground.

4 Mrs Johnson has a packet of currants which
weighs 2 kilograms.
If she uses 0.25 kg for making a cake, what weight
of currants will be left in the packet?

5 I go to the grocer's shop and buy the following.

half a kilogram of cheese	£2.05
half a kilogram of butter	£1.20
one loaf of bread	£0.78
six eggs	£0.82

If I pay with a £5 note, how much change should
I receive?

6 I have to make a picture frame like the one
illustrated.

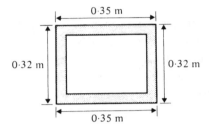

0·35 m

0·32 m

0·32 m

0·35 m

I have a piece of wood which is 1 metre in length.
Can I use this piece of wood for making three
sides of the picture frame?
Which three sides can I make?

7 Peter cycles from York to Scarborough. The
distance on the tripmeter fitted to his bicycle
shows the following figures before and after the
journey:

At York   3212.4 km
At Scarborough   3280.2 km

At a later date his father makes the same journey
by car. The tripmeter on the car shows the
following figures:

At York   37 986.7 km
At Scarborough   38 054.5 km

Are the two tripmeters accurate?
If so, what is the distance from York to
Scarborough?

Unit 2 Area, perimeter and volume

Area and perimeter

The perimeter of a shape is the total distance round the outside of the shape.

The area of a shape is the size of the surface covered by the shape.

The square has a perimeter of 4 cm and an area of 1 square centimetre (written 1 cm²).

Each side of the square is 1 cm long.
The diagonal of the square is approximately 1.4 cm long.

This half square has a perimeter of 3.4 cm (1 cm + 1 cm + 1.4 cm) and an area of $\frac{1}{2}$ cm².

Example 1

Find the perimeter and area of each of the following shapes.
Each square has an area of 1 cm².

a 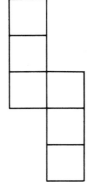   **b**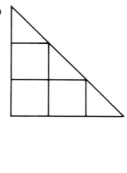

a has perimeter 14 cm and area 6 cm².

b has a perimeter of 6 whole sides and 3 diagonals, so its perimeter is

$$6 + 1.4 + 1.4 + 1.4 = 10.2 \text{ cm}$$

It has an area of 3 whole squares and 3 half squares, so its area is

$$3 + 1\frac{1}{2} = 4\frac{1}{2} \text{ cm}^2$$

Exercise 2.1

Find the perimeter and area of each of the following shapes.
Each square has an area of 1 cm².

1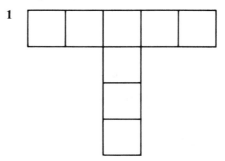

2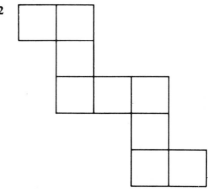

3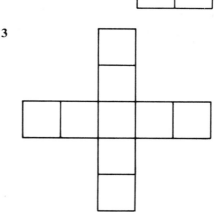

4

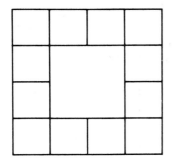

5

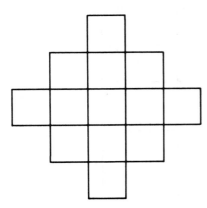

6

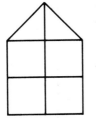

7

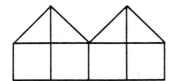

8

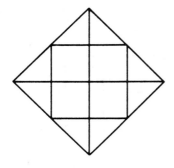

9

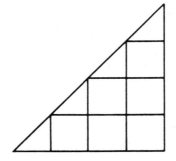

10

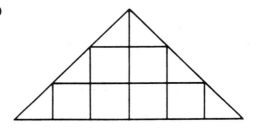

Exercise 2.2

Each of the following words has been drawn on a centimetre grid.
Find the perimeter and area of each letter.

1

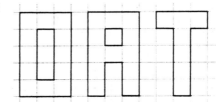

2

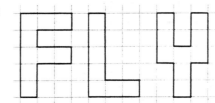

3

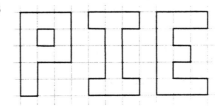

10

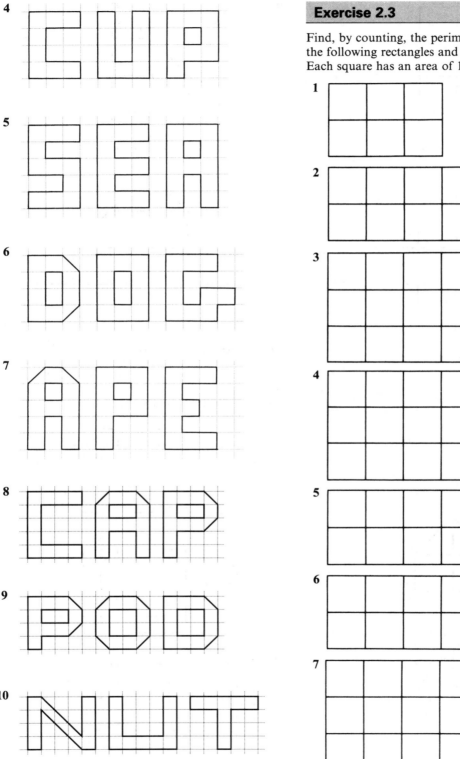

4

5

6

7

8

9

10

Exercise 2.3

Find, by counting, the perimeter and area of each of the following rectangles and squares.
Each square has an area of 1 cm².

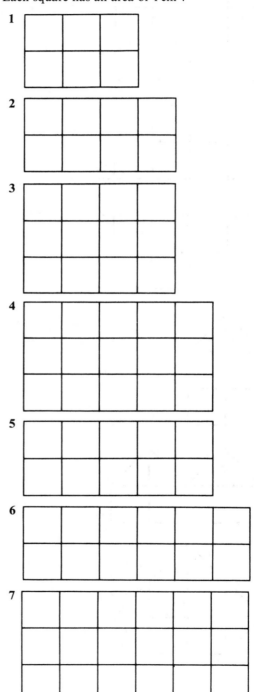

1

2

3

4

5

6

7

8

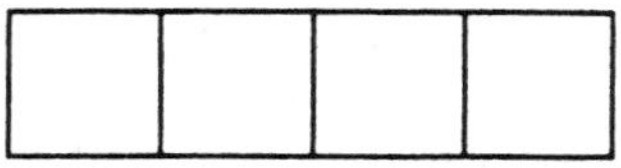

9

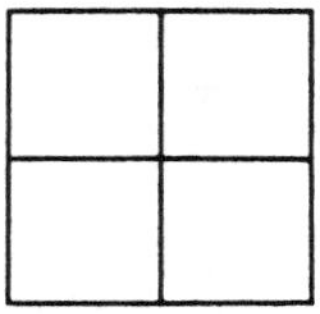

10

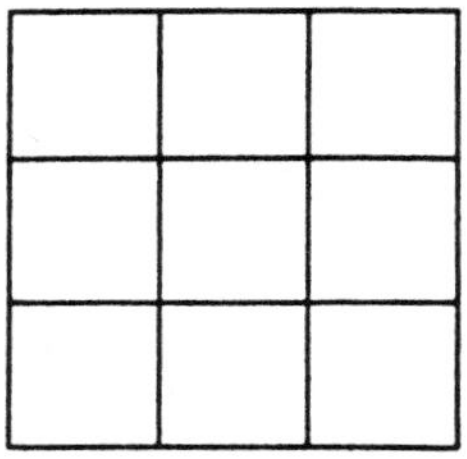

Exercise 2.4

You have 16 square pieces of card, each an exact square centimetre. The pieces of card are to be arranged to make a shape.
For example, the cards could be arranged like this

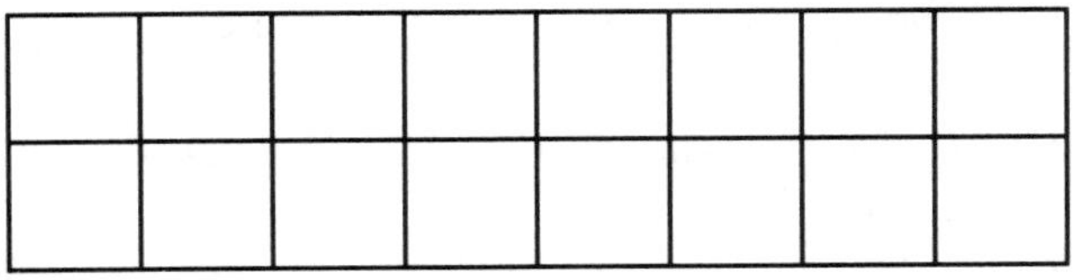

or like this

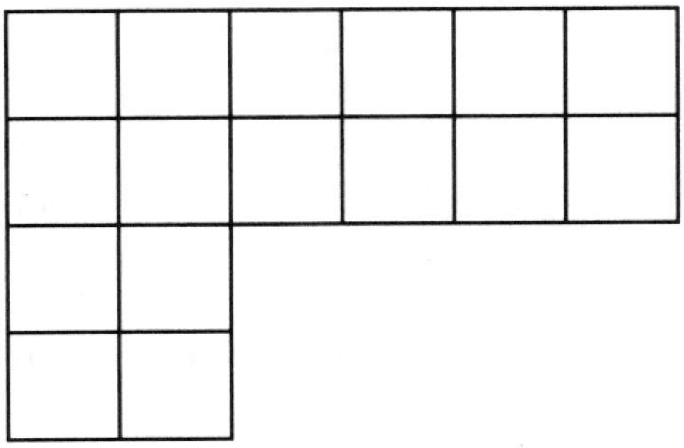

There must not be any 'holes' in the shape, like this

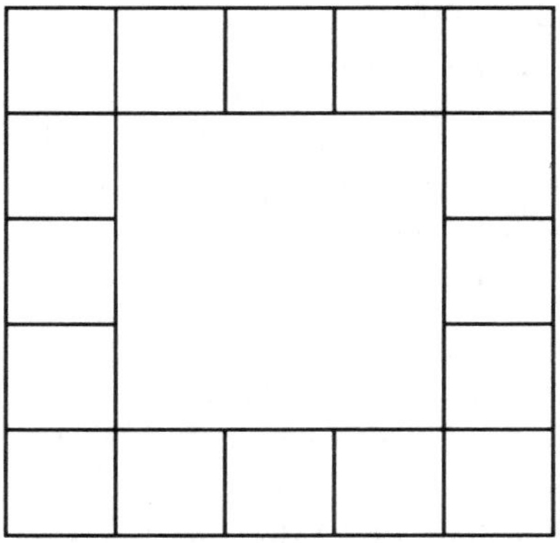

And the cards must be joined along a full edge like this

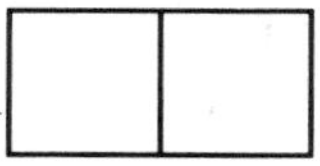

not like this

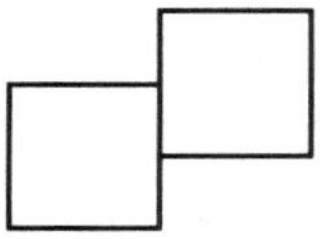

1 a Draw a picture to show how you would arrange the cards to form a shape with the greatest possible perimeter.
  b Draw a picture to show how you would arrange the cards to form a shape with the least possible perimeter.

2 Repeat question **1** with 9 pieces of card.

3 Repeat question **1** with 12 pieces of card.

4 You have a piece of string 16 cm long.
  a Draw a picture to show how you would arrange the string to form a shape with the **greatest** possible area.
  b Draw a picture to show how you would arrange the string to form a shape with the **least** possible area.

5 Repeat question **4** with 9 cm of string.

6 Repeat question **4** with 12 cm of string.

The *area* of a rectangle can be found by counting squares.

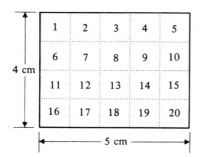

But it is easier to find the length and the width, and multiply them together to find the area. Both the length and the width must be in the same units.

The area of the rectangle above is

$$\text{length} \times \text{width} = 5 \times 4 = 20\,\text{cm}^2$$

The units of area are

square millimetres, mm^2
square centimetres, cm^2
square metres, m^2
or   square kilometres, km^2

Exercise 2.5

Write down the most suitable unit for the area of the following:

1 A domino
2 A playing card
3 A carpet
4 A door
5 The rectangle formed by the lines joining Annan, Longtown, Carlisle and Newton Arlosh

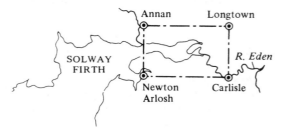

6 The square end of a match stick
7 The face of a small dice
8 A garden lawn
9 A ruler
10 A postage stamp

Example 2

Find the area and the perimeter of the following rectangles.

a 9 mm, 12 mm

b 25 mm, 6 cm

c 1.2 m, 1.2 m

a Area $= 12\,\text{mm} \times 9\,\text{mm}$
    $= 108\,\text{mm}^2$
Perimeter $= 12\,\text{mm} + 9\,\text{mm} + 12\,\text{mm} + 9\,\text{mm}$
    $= 42\,\text{mm}$

b Area $= 25\,\text{mm} \times 6\,\text{cm}$
    $= 2.5\,\text{cm} \times 6\,\text{cm}$
    $= 15\,\text{cm}^2$
Perimeter $= 2.5\,\text{cm} + 6\,\text{cm} + 2.5\,\text{cm} + 6\,\text{cm}$
    $= 17\,\text{cm}$

c Area $= 1.2\,\text{m} \times 1.2\,\text{m}$
    $= 1.44\,\text{m}^2$
Perimeter $= (1.2 + 1.2 + 1.2 + 1.2)\,\text{m}$
    $= 4.8\,\text{m}$

Example 3

Find the missing measurements for these rectangles.

	length	width	area	perimeter
a	12 cm	5 cm		
b	12 cm		36 cm^2	
c	12 cm			36 cm

a Area $= 12 \times 5 = 60\,\text{cm}^2$
    Perimeter $= 12 + 5 + 12 + 5 = 34\,\text{cm}$

b length $\times$ width $=$ area
    so width $= 3\,\text{cm}$ because $12 \times 3 = 36$
    $\therefore$ Perimeter $= 12 + 3 + 12 + 3 = 30\,\text{cm}$

c Perimeter $=$ length $+$ width $+$ length $+$ width
    $= 36\,\text{cm}$
    So width $= 6\,\text{cm}$ because $12 + 6 + 12 + 6$
    $= 36$
    $\therefore$ Area $= 12 \times 6 = 72\,\text{cm}^2$

Exercise 2.6

For each of the following find which rectangle has a different area from the other two.

1 a
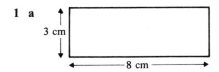

b
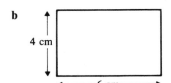

c
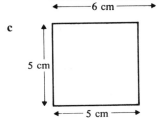

2 a
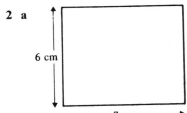

b   c
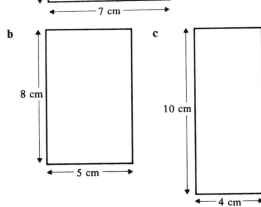

3 a
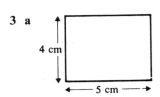

b
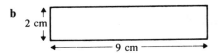

c
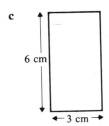

4 a
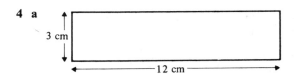

b
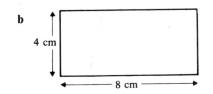

c
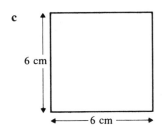

5 a length = 6 cm, width = 5 cm
  b length = 7 cm, width = 4 cm
  c length = 15 cm, width = 2 cm

6 a length = 12 cm, width = 40 mm
  b length = 9 cm, width = 50 mm
  c length = 80 mm, width = 60 mm

7 a length = 12 cm, width = 50 mm
  b length = 100 mm, width = 60 mm
  c length = 90 mm, width = 70 mm

Exercise 2.7

For each question in Exercise 2.6, find which rectangle has a different perimeter from the other two.

Exercise 2.8

Copy and complete the following table:

	length	width	area	perimeter
1	9 cm	4 cm		
2	7 cm	8 cm		
3	6 cm	9 cm		
4	5 cm	7 cm		
5	12 cm	6 cm		
6	12 cm	8 cm		
7	30 mm	50 mm		
8	80 mm	90 mm		
9	1.8 m	0.5 m		
10	1.5 m	1.2 m		
11	8 cm		48 cm²	
12	9 cm		27 cm²	
13	12 cm		60 cm²	
14	50 mm		2000 mm²	
15	25 mm		100 mm²	
16		5 cm	45 cm²	
17		6 cm	42 cm²	
18		7 cm	84 cm²	
19		4 m	60 m²	
20		3 m	75 m²	
21	6 cm			16 cm
22	7 cm			22 cm
23	10 cm			32 cm
24	40 mm			120 mm
25	15 mm			40 mm
26		4 cm		20 cm
27		3 cm		22 cm
28		9 cm		38 cm
29		4 m		18 m
30		5 m		26 m

Example 4

Find **a** the area, **b** the perimeter of the shape illustrated.

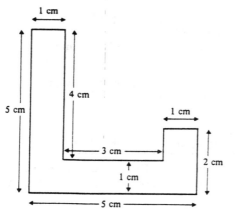

The area is found by dividing the shape into three rectangles as shown in the lower diagram and then adding together the three separate areas.

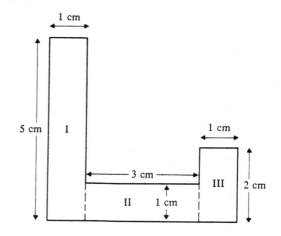

Area of rectangle   I $= 5 \times 1 = 5\,cm^2$

Area of rectangle II $= 3 \times 1 = 3\,cm^2$

Area of rectangle III $= 2 \times 1 = 2\,cm^2$

Therefore, area of the shape

$= 5\,cm^2 + 3\,cm^2 + 2\,cm^2 = 10\,cm^2$

Perimeter of the shape

$= 5 + 5 + 2 + 1 + 1 + 3 + 4 + 1 = 22\,cm$

Exercise 2.9

Find **a** the area, **b** the perimeter of the following shapes.

1

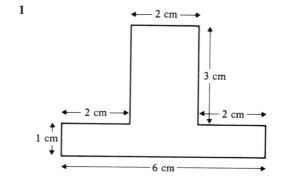

2

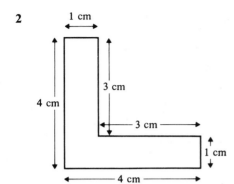

3

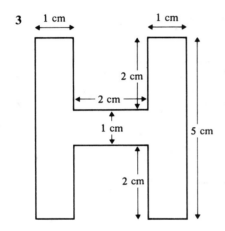

4

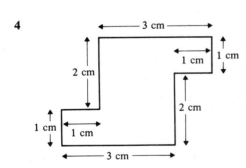

5

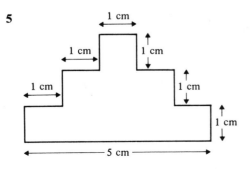

The area of each of the three triangles below is $6\,\text{cm}^2$.

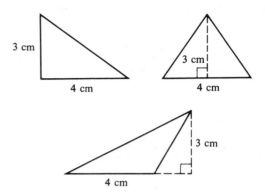

Area (of a triangle) $= \frac{1}{2} \times$ (length of base)
$\times$ (height)
$= \frac{1}{2} \times 4 \times 3$
$= 6\,\text{cm}^2$

Example 5

Find the area of each of the following triangles.

a

b

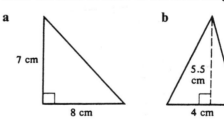

c

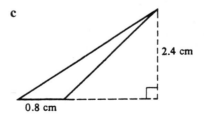

a Area $= \frac{1}{2} \times 8\,\text{cm} \times 7\,\text{cm} = 4 \times 7\,\text{cm} = 28\,\text{cm}^2$

b Area $= \frac{1}{2} \times 4\,\text{cm} \times 5.5\,\text{cm} = 2 \times 5.5$
$= 11.0\,\text{cm}^2$

c Area $= \frac{1}{2} \times 0.8\,\text{cm} \times 2.4\,\text{cm} = 0.4 \times 2.4$
$= 0.96\,\text{cm}^2$

Exercise 2.10

Find the area of each of the following triangles.

1
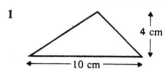
4 cm
10 cm

2

3 cm
12 cm

3
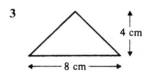
4 cm
8 cm

4
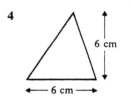
6 cm
6 cm

5
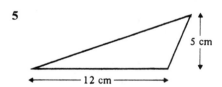
5 cm
12 cm

6
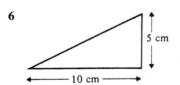
5 cm
10 cm

7
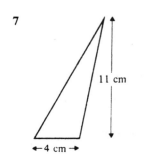
11 cm
4 cm

8
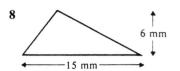
6 mm
15 mm

9
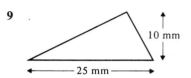
10 mm
25 mm

10
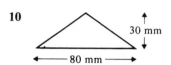
30 mm
80 mm

11
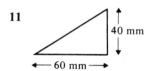
40 mm
60 mm

12
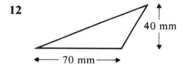
40 mm
70 mm

13
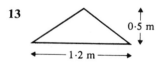
0·5 m
1·2 m

14
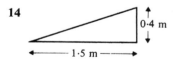
0·4 m
1·5 m

15
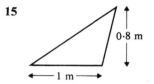
0·8 m
1 m

16
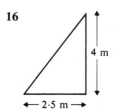
4 m
2·5 m

Example 6

At a sponsored 'Knit-In' a blanket 2.4 m by 1.5 m was made from square pieces with 15 cm sides. How many squares were knitted?

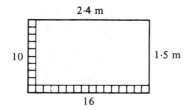

Blanket measures
(2.4×100) cm by (1.5×100) cm
$\quad = 240$ cm by 150 cm

Therefore, the no. of pieces along length
$\quad = 240 \div 15 = 16$
and, the no. of pieces along width
$\quad = 150 \div 15 = 10$
therefore, the no. of pieces altogether
$\quad = 16 \times 10 = 160$

Exercise 2.11

1 A square sheet of gift stamps measures 12 cm by 12 cm.
If each stamp measures 3 cm by 2 cm, how many does the sheet contain?

2 A wall space in a bathroom measures 1 m by 2 m, and it is to be covered with square tiles which measure 10 cm by 10 cm.
How many tiles are required?

3 A kitchen floor measures 6 m by 3 m, and it is to be covered with square tiles measuring 20 cm by 20 cm.
How many tiles are required?

4 A square lawn measures 4 m by 4 m, and it is to be covered with pieces of turf which measure 50 cm by 40 cm.
How many pieces of turf are required?

5 A square yard measures 6 m by 6 m, and it is to be covered with paving slabs which measure 1 m by 60 cm.
How many slabs are required?

Volume

Many well known objects are solids with mathematical names:

A sugar lump is a *cube*

A match box is a *cuboid*

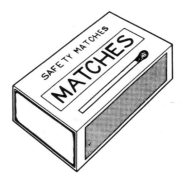

A tin of beans is a *cylinder*

Some tents are *triangular prisms*

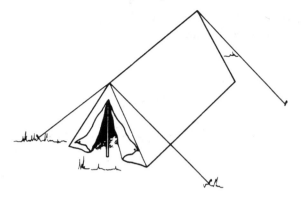

A football is a *sphere*

A dunce's cap is a *cone*

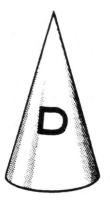

For each of the following, copy and complete the sentences by inserting the appropriate mathematical name.

1 A dice is a . . .

2 A brick is a . . .

3 A stick of seaside rock is a tall, thin . . .

4 A beefburger is a . . . which is nearly flat.

5 A cricket ball is a...

6 The piece of wood
holding this door
open is a...

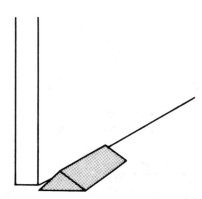

7 When this wine glass is
filled, the wine is poured
into a...

8 When water is poured into this drinking trough, it
is poured into a...

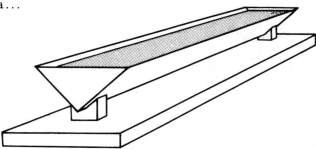

9 A cricket stump is a long, thin...with a...at one
end.

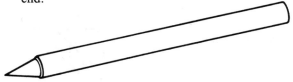

20

The amount of space which is filled by each of the objects drawn above is called its *volume*. The volume is measured in cubes and the common units are:

cubic millimetre (mm^3); cubic centimetre (cm^3) and cubic metre (m^3)

Example 7

Each cube has a volume of 1 cm^3. Find the volume of each of the following solids.

a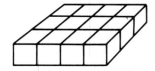

b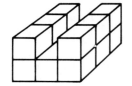

c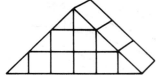

a Solid A is made up of 12 cubes, so its volume is 12 cm^3

b Solid B is made up of 15 cubes, so its volume is 15 cm^3

c Solid C is made up of 6 cubes and 6 half cubes, so its volume is
$6 + (\frac{1}{2} \times 6) = 6 + 3 = 9$ cm^3

For each of the following find which solid has a different volume from the other two.

1 a 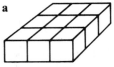   b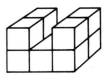

c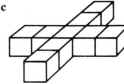

2 a 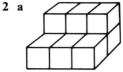   b

c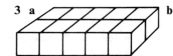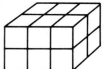

3 a 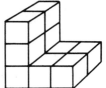   b

c

4 a 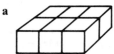   b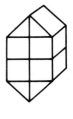

c

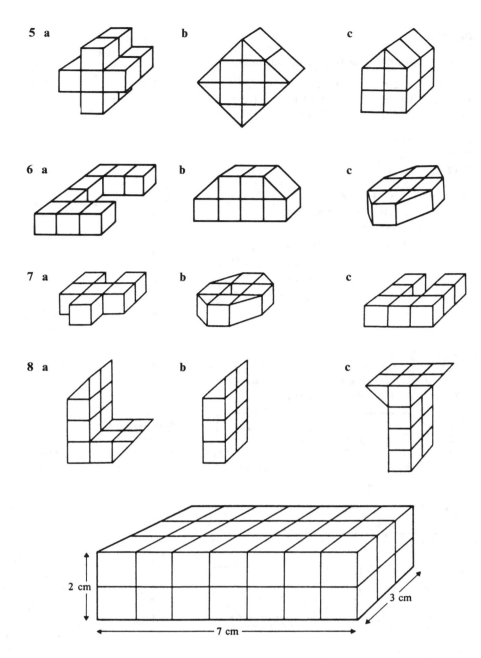

Instead of counting the number of cubes, the volume of a cuboid can be found by multiplying the length by the width by the height, provided each one is measured in the same units.

For the cuboid above:

volume = length (L) × width (W) × height (H)

$$= 7\,\text{cm} \times 3\,\text{cm} \times 2\,\text{cm} = 42\,\text{cm}^3$$

Example 8

Find the volume of the following cuboids.

a length $= 10\,\text{cm}$ **b** length $= 30\,\text{mm}$
width $= 10\,\text{cm}$ width $= 30\,\text{mm}$
height $= 10\,\text{cm}$ height $= 4\,\text{cm}$

c length $= 4\,\text{m}$
width $= 2.5\,\text{m}$
height $= 1.5\,\text{m}$

a volume $= L \times W \times H$
$\quad\quad\quad = 10\,\text{cm} \times 10\,\text{cm} \times 10\,\text{cm}$
$\quad\quad\quad = 1000\,\text{cm}^3$

b volume $= L \times W \times H = 30\,\text{m} \times 30\,\text{m} \times 4\,\text{m}$
$\quad\quad\quad\quad\quad\quad\quad\quad\quad = 3\,\text{cm} \times 3\,\text{cm} \times 4\,\text{cm}$
$\quad\quad\quad\quad\quad\quad\quad\quad\quad = 36\,\text{cm}^3$

c volume $= L \times W \times H = 4\,\text{m} \times 2.5\,\text{m} \times 1.5\,\text{m}$
$\quad\quad\quad\quad\quad\quad\quad\quad\quad = 10 \times 1.5$
$\quad\quad\quad\quad\quad\quad\quad\quad\quad = 15\,\text{m}^3$

Exercise 2.14

For each of the following find which cuboid has a different volume from the other two.

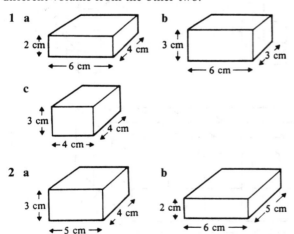

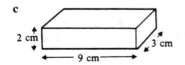

		length	width	height
3	**a**	12 cm	3 cm	2 cm
	b	8 cm	2 cm	4 cm
	c	4 cm	4 cm	4 cm

		length	width	height
4	**a**	6 cm	6 cm	2 cm
	b	8 cm	2 cm	5 cm
	c	3 cm	3 cm	8 cm
5	**a**	7 cm	2 cm	6 cm
	b	10 cm	4 cm	2 cm
	c	4 cm	4 cm	5 cm
6	**a**	3 cm	3 cm	10 cm
	b	9 cm	5 cm	2 cm
	c	7 cm	4 cm	3 cm
7	**a**	8 cm	3 cm	5 cm
	b	12 cm	3 cm	3 cm
	c	9 cm	6 cm	2 cm
8	**a**	2 cm	2 cm	50 mm
	b	10 mm	3 cm	8 cm
	c	40 mm	20 mm	30 mm
9	**a**	20 mm	3 cm	6 cm
	b	40 mm	40 mm	2 cm
	c	9 cm	20 mm	20 mm
10	**a**	3 m	1 m	0.5 m
	b	2 m	0.6 m	1 m
	c	1.5 m	2 m	0.4 m

Example 9

A cuboid has a volume of $72\,\text{cm}^3$.
If its length is $6\,\text{cm}$, and its width is $4\,\text{cm}$, find its height.

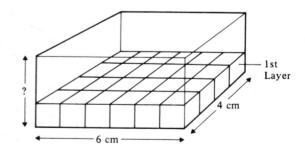

Number of $1\,\text{cm}^3$ cubes in the first layer

$$= 6 \times 4 = 24$$

Therefore, the number of such layers required to fill the cuboid

$$= 72 \div 24 = 3$$

Therefore, the height of the cuboid is $3\,\text{cm}$.

Exercise 2.15

Copy and complete the following table.

	length	width	height	volume
1	5 cm	2 cm		30 cm³
2	8 cm	2 cm		32 cm³
3	5 cm		2 cm	40 cm³
4	10 cm		2 cm	60 cm³
5		2 cm	3 cm	48 cm³
6		5 cm	2 cm	70 cm³
7	5 cm	30 mm		75 cm³
8	6 cm	30 mm		72 cm³
9	50 mm		4 cm	100 cm³
10	60 mm		5 cm	90 cm³
11		5 cm	40 mm	120 cm³
12		6 cm	10 mm	72 cm³
13	1 m	0.5 m		2 m³
14	0.4 m		1 m	1.2 m³
15		1 m	2.4 m	1.2 m³

An oil storage tank
as illustrated measures
2 m by $1\frac{1}{2}$ m by 1 m,
and has a volume of

$2 \times 1\frac{1}{2} \times 1 = 3\,\text{m}^3$.

Its capacity is
therefore 3000 litres
of oil, because

$1\,\text{m}^3 = 1000$ litres.

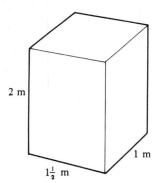

2 m

1 m

$1\frac{1}{2}$ m

The amount of liquid (in this case oil) which the
tank contains when full is called its *capacity*.

The *unit* of capacity is the litre.

1 litre = 1000 cm³.

5 ml

Smaller quantities, such as a dose of medicine,
are measured in millilitres (ml). A full teaspoon,
for example, contains approximately 5 ml.

1000 ml = 1 litre,

so a millilitre is the same as a cubic centimetre.

Example 10

Write as litres:

a 2500 cm³   **b** 3.75 m³   **c** 25 ml

a 2500 cm³ = 2500 ÷ 1000 litres = 2.5 litres
b 3.75 m³ = 3.75 × 1000 litres = 3750 litres
c 25 ml = 25 ÷ 1000 litres = 0.025 litres

Exercise 2.16

Write as litres:

1 4000 cm³	2 6000 cm³	3 3000 ml
4 10 000 cm³	5 12 000 cm³	6 7500 cm³
7 4500 cm³	8 1500 ml	9 6300 cm³
10 2400 ml	11 5 m³	12 8 m³
13 2 m³	14 14 m³	15 10 m³
16 2.5 m³	17 4.2 m³	18 6.25 m³
19 1.25 m³	20 8.75 m³	21 750 ml
22 450 ml	23 600 ml	24 900 cm³
25 65 ml	26 45 ml	27 15 cm³
28 20 ml	29 80 cm³	30 10 ml

Example 11

Find the capacity in litres of each of the
following tanks.

a $L = 30$ cm   **b** $L = 3$ m   **c** $L = 4$ m
    $W = 10$ cm $W = 4$ m $W = 50$ cm
    $H = 20$ cm $H = 2$ m $H = 20$cm

a $V = 30\,\text{cm} \times 10\,\text{cm} \times 20\,\text{cm} = 6000\,\text{cm}^3$,
    therefore, capacity = 6000 ÷ 1000 litres
                   = 6 litres

b $V = 3\,\text{m} \times 4\,\text{m} \times 2\,\text{m} = 24\,\text{m}^3$,
    therefore, capacity = 24 × 1000 litres
                   = 24 000 litres

c Volume (in m³) = $4 \times 0.5 \times 0.2 = 0.4\,\text{m}^3$,
    therefore, capacity = 0.4 × 1000 litres
                   = 400 litres

Exercise 2.17

Find the capacity in litres of each of the following
tanks.

1 $L = 40$ cm	**2** $L = 30$ cm	**3** $L = 50$ cm
$W = 20$ cm	$W = 20$ cm	$W = 30$ cm
$H = 10$ cm	$H = 20$ cm	$H = 20$ cm
4 $L = 40$ cm	**5** $L = 50$ cm	**6** $L = 5$ m
$W = 30$ cm	$W = 30$ cm	$W = 4$ m
$H = 10$ cm	$H = 30$ cm	$H = 3$ m

7	$L = 4\,m$	8	$L = 3\,m$	9	$L = 4\,m$
	$W = 3\,m$		$W = 3\,m$		$W = 2\,m$
	$H = 1\,m$		$H = 2\,m$		$H = 2\,m$
10	$L = 5\,m$	11	$L = 2\,m$	12	$L = 1\,m$
	$W = 3\,m$		$W = 50\,cm$		$W = 60\,cm$
	$H = 2\,m$		$H = 40\,cm$		$H = 50\,cm$
13	$L = 2\,m$	14	$L = 3\,m$	15	$L = 2\,m$
	$W = 60\,cm$		$W = 1\,m$		$W = 1.5\,m$
	$H = 1\,m$		$H = 50\,cm$		$H = 60\,cm$

Example 12

How many 5 ml spoonfuls of medicine can be taken from a bottle with a capacity of 150 ml? If you have to take 3 spoonfuls a day, how long will the bottle last?

Number of spoonfuls in the bottle

$$= 150 \div 5 = 30$$

Number of days

$$= 30 \div 3 = 10$$

So the bottle will last 10 days.

Exercise 2.18

1 The water tank in a house has a square base measuring 40 cm by 40 cm.
If it is filled with water to a depth of 50 cm, how many litres does it contain?

2 A rectangular coffee urn has a base which measures 30 cm by 25 cm, and it is 40 cm high.
How many litres of coffee does it contain when full?
How many cups, each of capacity 200 ml, can be filled from the urn when full?

3 At a café, orange squash is served from a plastic container with a square base that measures 40 cm by 40 cm.
If the orange squash is poured in to a depth of 15 cm, how many litres are in the container?
How many glasses, each of capacity 250 ml, can now be filled?

4 A paraffin can has a rectangular base measuring 30 cm by 25 cm, and it is filled to a depth of 60 cm.
How many times can the tank of a heater be filled from this quantity of paraffin if the tank measures 25 cm by 20 cm by 10 cm?

Exercise 2.19

1 If each square on the bingo card illustrated has an area of 1 cm², what is the area of the whole card?

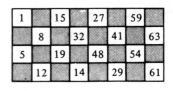

2 The illustration shows a pocket chess board which fits into a box.
If each square on the playing surface has an area of 1 cm², what is the area of the playing surface?
If the two spaces at the ends each have an area equal to $\frac{1}{4}$ of the area of the playing surface, what is the area of the whole board?

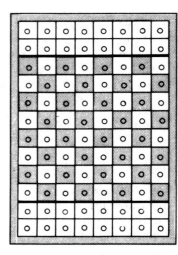

3 The illustration shows a teapot stand which has a decorative pattern of coloured squares.
If the area of each coloured square is equal to 1 cm², find the area of the teapot stand.

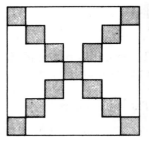

4 The illustration shows a table mat which has a decorative pattern.
If each coloured square has an area of 1 cm², find:
a the total area that is coloured.
b the area of the whole mat.

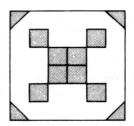

5 A number of dice fit exactly into a box as shown. If the volume of each die is 1 cm³, what is the volume of the box?

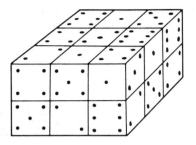

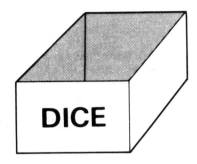

6 The illustration shows the arrangement of the sugar cubes which exactly fit into a packet. If each sugar cube has a volume of 1 cm³, what is the volume of the packet?

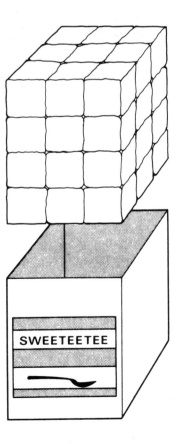

7 A small oil can has dimensions 10 cm by 7.5 cm by 4 cm.
  a Find its volume in cm³.
  b Find its capacity in millilitres.
  c Find its capacity in litres.

8 A car has a petrol tank whose dimensions are 80 cm by 25 cm by 20 cm.
How far can the car be driven on a full tank if it consumes one litre of petrol for every 12 km travelled?

9 A woman is driving a car which suddenly runs out of petrol. In the boot of the car is a full can of petrol which measures 25 cm by 15 cm by 8 cm. If the woman is 50 km from home and her car travels 17 km on every litre of petrol, has she enough to get home?

10 The picture shows the dimensions of a paddling pool.

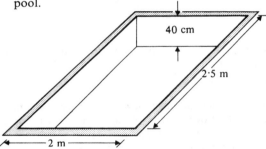

  a Find the volume of the paddling pool in cubic metres.
  b How many litres of water are required to fill the pool?

11 The dimensions of a cattle trough are shown below.

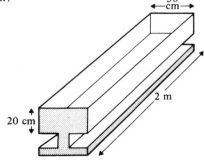

  a Find the volume of the cattle trough in cubic metres.
  b What is the capacity of the trough in litres?
  c The trough is filled using a bucket of capacity 25 litres.
  How many full buckets are required?

12 Lucy has made some toffee in a tray which measures 30 cm by 15 cm. She cuts the toffee into square pieces which measure 3 cm by 3 cm. How many pieces will there be?

13 A man wants to pave an area near his back door measuring 2 m by 1.2 m. He has paving stones which measure 60 cm by 40 cm. How many paving stones will he require?

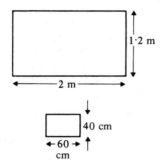

Draw a diagram to show how to arrange the paving stones.

14 The entrance hall to a new house measures 6 m by 1.5 m. Its floor is to be made from wooden boards measuring 200 cm by 15 cm. How many boards will be required?

15 The diagram shows a wire mesh guard for an electric fire.

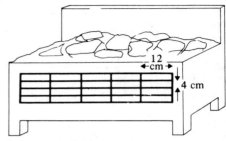

Find the area of this guard.

16 a Find the area and the perimeter of the square illustrated below.

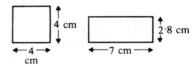

b Find the area and the perimeter of the rectangle shown above.
c What property do the square and the rectangle have in common?
d If the rectangle shown below is also to have this property, what is its width?

Unit 3 Rotation

Rotational symmetry

Some shapes fit into the same position more than once when rotated through 360 degrees. For example:

When this happens, the shape is said to have *rotational symmetry*.

The *order of rotational symmetry* is the number of times the shape fits into the same position.

In this case the shape has an order of rotational symmetry of 3.

Shapes with no rotational symmetry only fit once and have an order of rotational symmetry of 1.

Example 1

Which one of the following shapes is different from the others, i.e. has no rotational symmetry?

State the order of rotational symmetry for each shape.

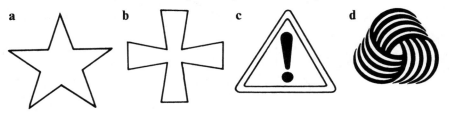

The one that is different is **c** because it has no rotational symmetry.

The orders of rotational symmetry are

| **a** 5 | **b** 4 | **c** 1 | **d** 3 |

28

For each of the following, find which shape is different from the others, i.e. has no rotational symmetry.

State the order of rotational symmetry for each shape.

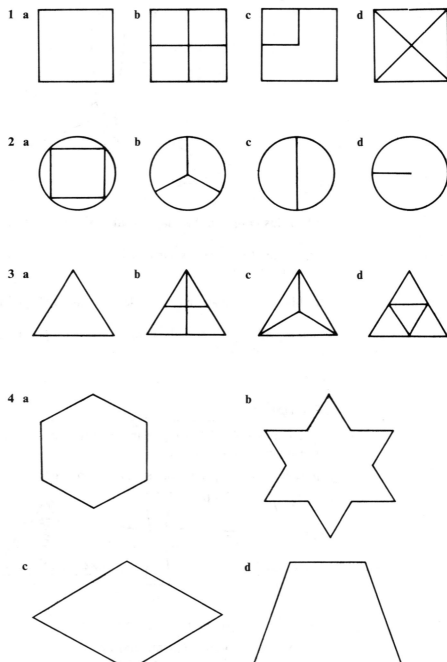

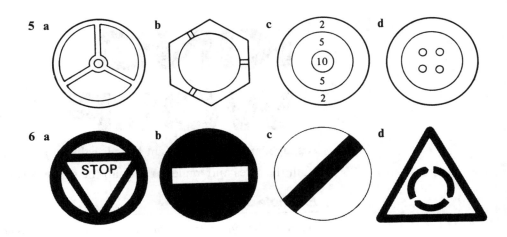

Example 2

Describe the symmetry of each letter in the word:

SHARE

S has rotational symmetry only
H has rotational symmetry and two lines of symmetry
A has one line of symmetry only
R has no symmetry
E has one line of symmetry only.

Exercise 3.2

Describe the symmetry of each letter in the following words.

1 **DAISY**

2 **YACHT**

3 **ZEBRA**

4 **MIXER**

⁵ KING
⁶ WOLF

A shape enclosed by straight lines is called a *polygon*.

If all the sides and angles are equal, the shape is called a *regular polygon*.

Example 3

Describe the symmetry of this regular four sided polygon
(square).

The square has four lines of symmetry and rotational
symmetry of order 4.

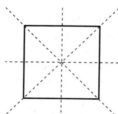

Exercise 3.3

Describe the symmetry of each regular polygon.

1 A regular
heptagon

2 A regular
pentagon

3 A regular
hexagon

4 An equilateral
triangle

5 A regular
octagon

6 A regular
dodecagon

7 A regular
decagon

8 A regular
nonagon

Example 4

Describe the symmetry of this regular shape.

It has two lines of symmetry and rotational symmetry of order 2.

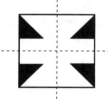

Exercise 3.4

Describe the symmetry of each shape.

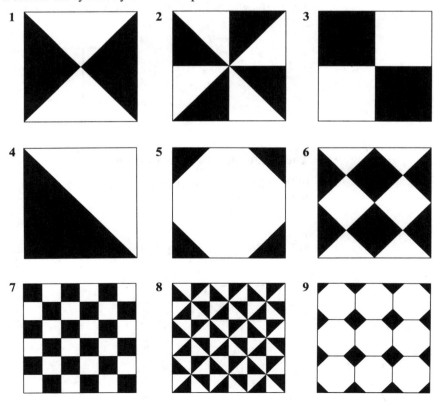

Rotation

The change in position of an object is known as a *transformation*. We have looked at reflection in which an object is transformed to its mirror image. Rotation is another kind of transformation.

The object is rotated about a fixed point (the centre of rotation) to form the image.

Example 5

Copy the shape below on to graph paper or squared paper.

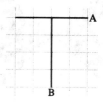

Then draw the image formed by rotating the object

a 90° clockwise about A
b 90° clockwise about B

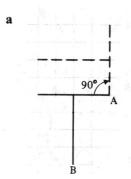

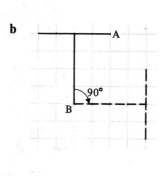

Exercise 3.5

Copy the object shown in each question on to graph paper or squared paper.
Then draw the image formed by rotating the object clockwise through 90° about
(i) A;   (ii) B.
Draw a separate diagram for each rotation.

1

2
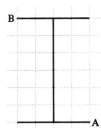

3
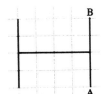

4

5

6

7
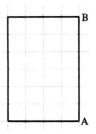

8
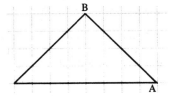

9
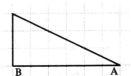

10
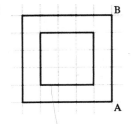

Clockwise rotations are *negative*.

Anticlockwise rotations are *positive*.

Example 6

Copy the shape below.

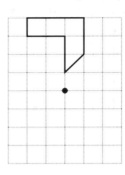

Then draw the image formed by rotating the object

a +90° about the dot

b −90° about the dot

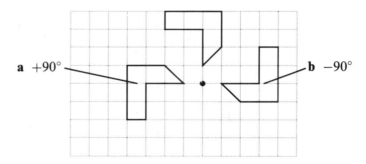

Exercise 3.6

Copy each diagram on to squared paper.
Then draw the image formed by rotating the object
through the given angle about the marked dot.

1 +90°

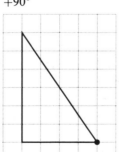

2 −90°

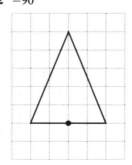

3 180°

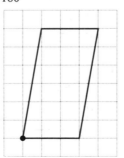

4 +270°

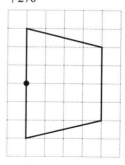

5 −270°

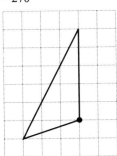

6 +90°

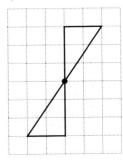

7 −90°

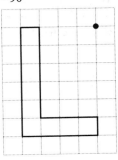

8 180°

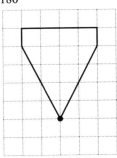

9 +270°

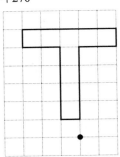

10 −270°

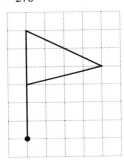

11 180°

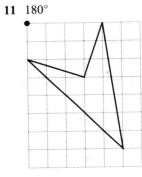

12 180°

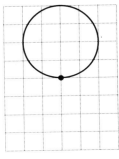

13 +90°

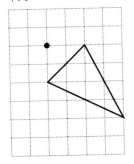

14 −90°

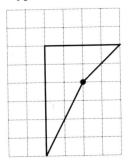

15 +270°

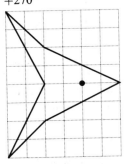

16 180°

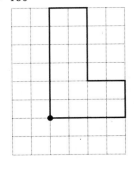

17 −270°

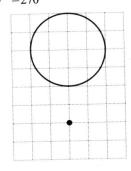

18 +270°

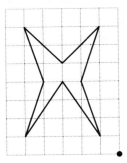

19 +90°

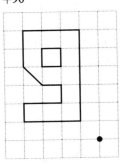

20 −90°

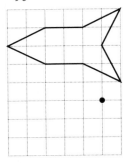

Example 7

Copy the triangle ABC on to graph paper or squared paper.

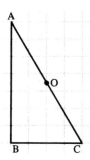

Then draw the image formed

a when the triangle is reflected along the line AC,
b when the triangle is rotated through 180° about O, the mid-point of AC.

Name the figure produced in each case.

a

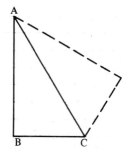

b

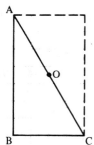

a The shape is a kite.
b The shape is a rectangle.

Exercise 3.7

For questions **1** to **4**, copy the triangle ABC on to graph paper or squared paper.
Then draw the image of the triangle formed

a by reflection in the line BC,
b by rotation through 180° about O.

Name the figure produced in each case.

1

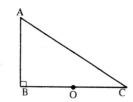

2

3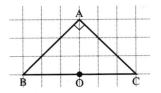

4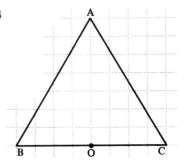

5 Make two copies of the figure ABCD on graph paper or squared paper.

Then draw the image of the shape formed

a by reflection in the line BC,
b by rotation through 180° about O.

Name the figure produced in each case.

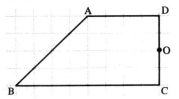

For questions **6** to **8**, copy the figure on to graph paper or squared paper.
Then draw the image of the shape formed by rotation through +90° about O, the
centre of the figure.

6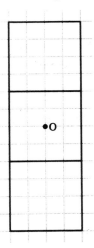

7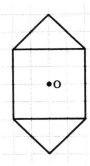

8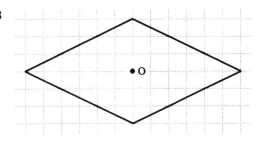

9 The illustration shows the equilateral triangle ABC and its image after rotation.

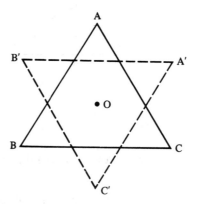

Has the triangle been rotated through −30°, −45° or −60°?

10 The illustration shows the square ABCD and its image after rotation.

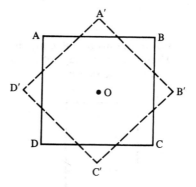

Has the square been rotated through −30°, −45° or −60°?

Unit 4　Fractions, percentages and decimals

Fractions

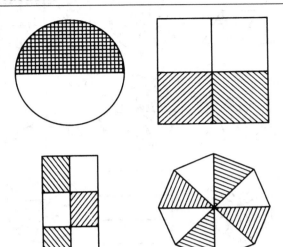

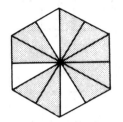

b

Number of parts shaded $= 9$
Number of equal parts $= 12$
Therefore, fraction $= \frac{9}{12} = \frac{3}{4}$

All of the above shapes have one half shaded.

$$\tfrac{1}{2} = \tfrac{2}{4} = \tfrac{3}{6} = \tfrac{4}{8}$$

Fractions having the same value are called *equivalent fractions*. Equivalent fractions can be found by two methods

a multiplying the top and the bottom by the same number.

e.g.　(i) $\dfrac{2}{3} = \dfrac{2 \times 2}{3 \times 2} = \dfrac{4}{6}$　(ii) $\dfrac{3}{5} = \dfrac{3 \times 6}{5 \times 6} = \dfrac{18}{30}$

b dividing the top and the bottom by the same number:

e.g.　(i) $\dfrac{4}{6} = \dfrac{4 \div 2}{6 \div 2} = \dfrac{2}{3}$

(ii) $\dfrac{18}{30} = \dfrac{18 \div 2}{30 \div 2} = \dfrac{9}{15} = \dfrac{9 \div 3}{15 \div 3} = \dfrac{3}{5}$

Example 1

Find the simplest form of the fraction shaded in each of these drawings

a

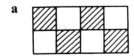

Number of parts shaded $= 4$
Number of equal parts $= 8$
Therefore, fraction $= \tfrac{4}{8} = \tfrac{1}{2}$

Exercise 4.1

Find the simplest form of the fraction shaded in each of these drawings.

1

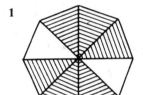

2

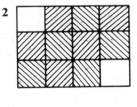

3

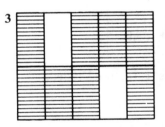

4

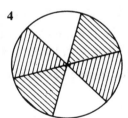

5

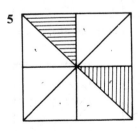

6

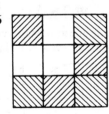

7

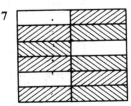

8

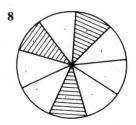

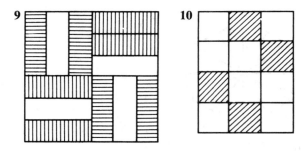

Example 2

Which of the three diagrams has a different fraction shaded?

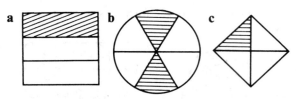

a 1 out of 3 parts is shaded.
Therefore, fraction $= \frac{1}{3}$

b 2 out of 6 parts are shaded.
Therefore, fraction $= \frac{2}{6} = \frac{1}{3}$

c 1 out of 4 parts are shaded.
Therefore, fraction $= \frac{1}{4}$

Therefore **c** has a different fraction shaded.

Exercise 4.2

For each question state which of the three diagrams has a different fraction shaded.

1 a **b** **c**

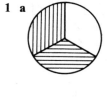 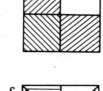

2 a **b** **c**

3 a **b** **c**

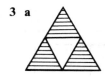 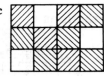

4 a **b** **c**

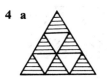 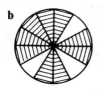

5 a **b** **c**

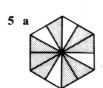 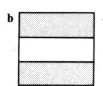

6 a **b** **c**

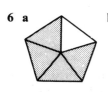 

7 a **b** **c**

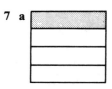

8 a **b** **c**

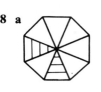

9 a **b** **c**

  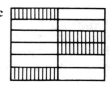

10 a **b** **c**

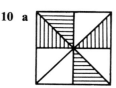 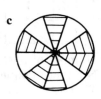

Example 3

Find which fraction is different from the other three.

a $\frac{4}{6}$ **b** $\frac{10}{15}$ **c** $\frac{10}{18}$ **d** $\frac{14}{21}$

In their simplest form

a $\dfrac{4}{6} = \dfrac{4 \div 2}{6 \div 2} = \dfrac{2}{3}$ **b** $\dfrac{10}{15} = \dfrac{10 \div 5}{15 \div 5} = \dfrac{2}{3}$

c $\dfrac{10}{18} = \dfrac{10 \div 2}{18 \div 2} = \dfrac{5}{9}$ **d** $\dfrac{14}{21} = \dfrac{14 \div 7}{21 \div 7} = \dfrac{2}{3}$

Therefore, **c** is different from the other three because it is not equivalent to $\frac{2}{3}$.

Exercise 4.3

For each question find which fraction is different from the others.

1 a $\frac{12}{16}$ **b** $\frac{18}{24}$ **c** $\frac{25}{30}$ **d** $\frac{27}{36}$

2 a $\frac{16}{24}$ **b** $\frac{18}{30}$ **c** $\frac{12}{18}$ **d** $\frac{30}{45}$

3 a $\frac{10}{12}$ **b** $\frac{40}{48}$ **c** $\frac{15}{18}$ **d** $\frac{21}{24}$

4 a $\frac{12}{30}$ **b** $\frac{10}{25}$ **c** $\frac{4}{10}$ **d** $\frac{15}{40}$

5 a $\frac{12}{36}$ **b** $\frac{8}{32}$ **c** $\frac{7}{28}$ **d** $\frac{4}{16}$

6 a $\frac{3}{15}$ **b** $\frac{7}{35}$ **c** $\frac{6}{30}$ **d** $\frac{5}{20}$

7 a $\frac{4}{24}$ **b** $\frac{6}{30}$ **c** $\frac{7}{42}$ **d** $\frac{3}{18}$

8 a $\frac{6}{18}$ **b** $\frac{15}{45}$ **c** $\frac{9}{36}$ **d** $\frac{4}{12}$

9 a $\frac{24}{30}$ **b** $\frac{20}{32}$ **c** $\frac{30}{48}$ **d** $\frac{10}{16}$

10 a $\frac{15}{36}$ **b** $\frac{6}{16}$ **c** $\frac{18}{48}$ **d** $\frac{12}{32}$

11 a $\frac{14}{16}$ **b** $\frac{40}{48}$ **c** $\frac{35}{40}$ **d** $\frac{21}{24}$

12 a $\frac{20}{36}$ **b** $\frac{28}{48}$ **c** $\frac{30}{54}$ **d** $\frac{10}{18}$

13 a $\frac{21}{27}$ **b** $\frac{25}{30}$ **c** $\frac{20}{24}$ **d** $\frac{30}{36}$

14 a $\frac{16}{48}$ **b** $\frac{5}{15}$ **c** $\frac{8}{18}$ **d** $\frac{18}{54}$

15 a $\frac{33}{36}$ **b** $\frac{42}{48}$ **c** $\frac{55}{60}$ **d** $\frac{22}{24}$

16 a $\frac{16}{18}$ **b** $\frac{25}{30}$ **c** $\frac{32}{36}$ **17 a** $\frac{12}{48}$ **b** $\frac{4}{12}$ **c** $\frac{9}{36}$

18 a $\frac{6}{40}$ **b** $\frac{4}{48}$ **c** $\frac{5}{60}$ **19 a** $\frac{15}{40}$ **b** $\frac{9}{24}$ **c** $\frac{21}{60}$

20 a $\frac{8}{60}$ **b** $\frac{12}{80}$ **c** $\frac{15}{100}$ **21 a** $\frac{16}{30}$ **b** $\frac{35}{60}$ **c** $\frac{48}{90}$

22 a $\frac{27}{60}$ **b** $\frac{21}{48}$ **c** $\frac{35}{80}$ **23 a** $\frac{26}{40}$ **b** $\frac{65}{100}$ **c** $\frac{55}{80}$

24 a $\frac{21}{36}$ **b** $\frac{27}{48}$ **c** $\frac{18}{32}$ **25 a** $\frac{25}{80}$ **b** $\frac{16}{60}$ **c** $\frac{20}{75}$

Example 4

Copy the diagrams and shade in $\frac{2}{3}$ of the pattern on each.

a 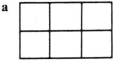   **b**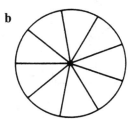

a There are 6 equal parts, so 4 parts have to be shaded because $\frac{4}{6} = \frac{2}{3}$.

b There are 9 equal parts, so 6 parts have to be shaded because $\frac{6}{9} = \frac{2}{3}$.

Exercise 4.4

1 Copy the diagrams and shade in $\frac{1}{2}$ the pattern on each.

   b   **c**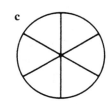

2 Copy the diagrams and shade in $\frac{1}{5}$ of the pattern on each.

   **b**

3 Copy the diagram and shade in $\frac{1}{3}$ of the pattern on each.

4 Copy the diagrams and shade in $\frac{1}{4}$ of the pattern on each.

a   **b**

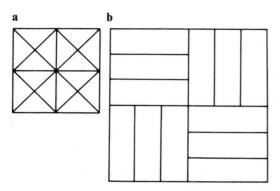

5 Copy the diagrams and shade in $\frac{1}{6}$ of the pattern on each.

a   **b**

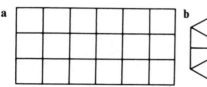

6 Copy the diagrams and shade in $\frac{2}{3}$ of the pattern on each.

a   **b**   **c**

7 Copy the diagrams and shade in $\frac{3}{4}$ of the pattern on each.

a   **b**

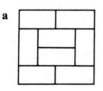

8 Copy the diagrams and shade in $\frac{3}{5}$ of the pattern on each.

a   **b**

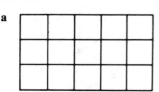
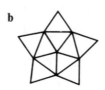

9 Copy the diagram and shade in $\frac{3}{8}$ of the pattern.

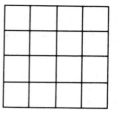

10 Copy the diagram and shade in $\frac{5}{8}$ of the pattern.

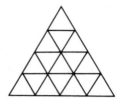

Exercise 4.5

Copy and complete by filling in the empty spaces.

1 $\frac{1}{3} = \frac{}{6}$ **2** $\frac{3}{4} = \frac{}{8}$ **3** $\frac{1}{2} = \frac{}{8}$ **4** $\frac{2}{5} = \frac{}{15}$

5 $\frac{1}{5} = \frac{}{20}$ **6** $\frac{3}{8} = \frac{}{32}$ **7** $\frac{1}{6} = \frac{}{30}$ **8** $\frac{5}{8} = \frac{}{40}$

9 $\frac{3}{5} = \frac{}{30}$ **10** $\frac{2}{3} = \frac{}{18}$ **11** $\frac{1}{4} = \frac{}{36}$ **12** $\frac{1}{5} = \frac{}{60}$

13 $\frac{1}{8} = \frac{2}{}$ **14** $\frac{7}{10} = \frac{14}{}$ **15** $\frac{1}{12} = \frac{3}{}$ **16** $\frac{4}{5} = \frac{12}{}$

17 $\frac{1}{9} = \frac{4}{}$ **18** $\frac{5}{7} = \frac{20}{}$ **19** $\frac{3}{8} = \frac{15}{}$ **20** $\frac{5}{6} = \frac{25}{}$

21 $\frac{3}{4} = \frac{18}{}$ **22** $\frac{2}{5} = \frac{14}{}$ **23** $\frac{4}{5} = \frac{32}{}$ **24** $\frac{2}{3} = \frac{24}{}$

25 $\frac{1}{4} = \frac{15}{}$ **26** $\frac{4}{6} = \frac{}{3}$ **27** $\frac{10}{12} = \frac{}{6}$ **28** $\frac{9}{15} = \frac{}{5}$

29 $\frac{21}{36} = \frac{}{12}$ **30** $\frac{16}{36} = \frac{}{5}$ **31** $\frac{32}{36} = \frac{}{9}$ **32** $\frac{5}{40} = \frac{}{8}$

33 $\frac{15}{35} = \frac{}{7}$ **34** $\frac{24}{30} = \frac{}{5}$ **35** $\frac{6}{24} = \frac{}{4}$ **36** $\frac{24}{32} = \frac{}{4}$

37 $\frac{48}{60} = \frac{}{5}$ **38** $\frac{18}{20} = \frac{9}{}$ **39** $\frac{14}{24} = \frac{7}{}$ **40** $\frac{15}{18} = \frac{5}{}$

41 $\frac{21}{33} = \frac{7}{}$ **42** $\frac{20}{32} = \frac{5}{}$ **43** $\frac{20}{48} = \frac{5}{}$ **44** $\frac{35}{60} = \frac{7}{}$

45 $\frac{40}{45} = \frac{8}{}$ **46** $\frac{30}{36} = \frac{5}{}$ **47** $\frac{6}{54} = \frac{1}{}$ **48** $\frac{45}{54} = \frac{5}{}$

49 $\frac{48}{108} = \frac{4}{}$ **50** $\frac{75}{100} = \frac{3}{}$ **51** $\frac{}{2} = \frac{5}{10}$ **52** $\frac{}{4} = \frac{9}{12}$

53 $\frac{}{8} = \frac{15}{40}$ **54** $\frac{}{12} = \frac{25}{60}$ **55** $\frac{}{15} = \frac{16}{60}$ **56** $\frac{1}{} = \frac{5}{20}$

57 $\frac{2}{} = \frac{8}{12}$ **58** $\frac{4}{} = \frac{24}{30}$ **59** $\frac{3}{} = \frac{45}{60}$ **60** $\frac{7}{} = \frac{35}{100}$

61 $\frac{}{15} = \frac{1}{3}$ **62** $\frac{}{20} = \frac{3}{5}$ **63** $\frac{}{30} = \frac{5}{6}$ **64** $\frac{}{60} = \frac{7}{12}$

65 $\frac{}{20} = \frac{45}{100}$ **66** $\frac{5}{} = \frac{1}{6}$ **67** $\frac{16}{} = \frac{2}{3}$ **68** $\frac{55}{} = \frac{11}{12}$

69 $\frac{24}{} = \frac{2}{5}$ **70** $\frac{15}{} = \frac{3}{20}$

The top number in a fraction is called the *numerator*; the bottom number is called the *denominator*.

An *improper fraction* is 'top-heavy': the numerator is greater than the denominator.

e.g. $\frac{4}{3}$, $\frac{23}{6}$, $\frac{18}{9}$

An improper fraction can be turned into a *mixed number*.

Example 5

Write as a mixed number

a $\frac{4}{3}$ **b** $\frac{23}{6}$ **c** $\frac{18}{9}$ **d** $\frac{14}{8}$

a $\frac{4}{3} = \frac{3}{3} + \frac{1}{3}$

$= 1 + \frac{1}{3}$

$= 1\frac{1}{3}$

b $\frac{23}{6} = \frac{6}{6} + \frac{6}{6} + \frac{6}{6} + \frac{5}{6}$

$= 1 + 1 + 1 + \frac{5}{6}$

$= 3\frac{5}{6}$

c $\frac{18}{9} = \frac{9}{9} + \frac{9}{9}$

$= 1 + 1$

$= 2$

d $\frac{14}{8} = \frac{8}{8} + \frac{6}{8}$

$= 1 + \frac{6}{8}$

$= 1\frac{6}{8}$

$= 1\frac{3}{4}$

Exercise 4.6

Write these improper fractions as mixed numbers.

1 $\frac{7}{6}$ **2** $\frac{9}{8}$ **3** $\frac{5}{3}$ **4** $\frac{10}{7}$ **5** $\frac{11}{6}$

6 $\frac{9}{5}$ **7** $\frac{13}{8}$ **8** $\frac{17}{10}$ **9** $\frac{14}{11}$ **10** $\frac{17}{12}$

11 $\frac{10}{8}$ **12** $\frac{10}{6}$ **13** $\frac{16}{10}$ **14** $\frac{8}{6}$ **15** $\frac{15}{12}$

16 $\frac{15}{9}$ **17** $\frac{24}{15}$ **18** $\frac{12}{8}$ **19** $\frac{20}{12}$ **20** $\frac{25}{15}$

21 $\frac{5}{2}$ **22** $\frac{9}{4}$ **23** $\frac{8}{3}$ **24** $\frac{14}{5}$ **25** $\frac{18}{8}$

26 $\frac{26}{10}$ **27** $\frac{15}{6}$ **28** $\frac{24}{9}$ **29** $\frac{14}{7}$ **30** $\frac{24}{8}$

31 $\frac{10}{3}$ **32** $\frac{13}{4}$ **33** $\frac{15}{4}$ **34** $\frac{14}{4}$ **35** $\frac{22}{6}$

36 $\frac{9}{2}$ **37** $\frac{14}{3}$ **38** $\frac{34}{8}$ **39** $\frac{21}{4}$ **40** $\frac{33}{6}$

Example 6

Write as an improper fraction

a $1\frac{1}{5}$ **b** $4\frac{7}{8}$ **c** 100

a $1\frac{1}{5} = 1 + \frac{1}{5}$

$= \frac{5}{5} + \frac{1}{5}$

$= \frac{6}{5}$

b $4\frac{7}{8} = 4 + \frac{7}{8}$

$= 1 + 1 + 1 + 1 + \frac{7}{8}$

$= \frac{8}{8} + \frac{8}{8} + \frac{8}{8} + \frac{8}{8} + \frac{7}{8}$

$= \frac{39}{8}$

c $100 = \frac{100}{1}$

To write a whole number as an improper fraction, put the number over a denominator of 1.

Exercise 4.7

Write these mixed numbers as improper fractions.

1 $1\frac{1}{4}$ **2** $1\frac{1}{9}$ **3** $1\frac{2}{5}$ **4** $1\frac{3}{8}$ **5** $1\frac{5}{7}$

6 $1\frac{3}{10}$ **7** $1\frac{7}{12}$ **8** $1\frac{7}{8}$ **9** $2\frac{1}{3}$ **10** $2\frac{1}{5}$

11 $2\frac{3}{4}$ **12** $2\frac{3}{5}$ **13** $2\frac{2}{7}$ **14** $3\frac{1}{2}$ **15** $3\frac{1}{5}$

16 $3\frac{2}{3}$ **17** $4\frac{1}{4}$ **18** $4\frac{3}{5}$ **19** $5\frac{1}{3}$ **20** $5\frac{2}{5}$

21 $5\frac{4}{5}$ **22** $5\frac{3}{4}$ **23** $6\frac{1}{2}$ **24** $6\frac{1}{3}$ **25** $7\frac{1}{2}$

26 3 **27** 8 **28** 15 **29** 40 **30** 1

Fractions and decimals

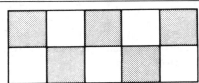

In the diagram $\frac{1}{2}$ or $\frac{5}{10}$ or 0.5 is shaded.

So $\frac{1}{2} = \frac{5}{10} = 0.5$

In the diagram $\frac{2}{5}$ or $\frac{4}{10}$ or 0.4 is shaded.

So $\frac{2}{5} = \frac{4}{10} = 0.4$

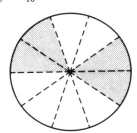

44

Fractions can easily be changed into decimals. Using a calculator, the top number of the fraction is divided by the bottom number of the fraction.

Example 7

Turn these fractions into decimals.

a $\frac{1}{4}$ **b** $\frac{3}{50}$ **c** $\frac{5}{8}$

a $1 \div 4 = 0.25$

So $\frac{1}{4} = 0.25$

b $3 \div 50 = 0.06$

So $\frac{3}{50} = 0.06$

c $5 \div 8 = 0.625$

So $\frac{5}{8} = 0.625$

Exercise 4.8

Turn each fraction into a decimal.

1 $\frac{1}{5}$	**2** $\frac{3}{5}$	**3** $\frac{1}{10}$	**4** $\frac{9}{10}$	**5** $\frac{9}{50}$
6 $\frac{13}{50}$	**7** $\frac{21}{50}$	**8** $\frac{27}{50}$	**9** $\frac{31}{50}$	**10** $\frac{43}{50}$
11 $\frac{39}{50}$	**12** $\frac{1}{50}$	**13** $\frac{3}{20}$	**14** $\frac{7}{20}$	**15** $\frac{13}{20}$
16 $\frac{19}{20}$	**17** $\frac{1}{20}$	**18** $\frac{4}{25}$	**19** $\frac{6}{25}$	**20** $\frac{9}{25}$
21 $\frac{12}{25}$	**22** $\frac{18}{25}$	**23** $\frac{2}{25}$	**24** $\frac{3}{4}$	**25** $\frac{61}{500}$
26 $\frac{53}{500}$	**27** $\frac{21}{200}$	**28** $\frac{51}{125}$	**29** $\frac{1}{8}$	**30** $\frac{7}{8}$

Using what you know about place value, a decimal fraction can easily be turned into a common fraction.

Example 8

Turn these decimals into fractions.

a 0.7 **b** 0.37 **c** 0.019

a $0.7 = \frac{7}{10}$

b $0.37 = \frac{3}{10} + \frac{7}{100} = \frac{30}{100} + \frac{7}{100} = \frac{37}{100}$

c $0.019 = \frac{0}{10} + \frac{1}{100} + \frac{9}{1000}$

$= \frac{10}{1000} + \frac{9}{1000}$

$= \frac{19}{1000}$

Exercise 4.9

Turn these decimals into fractions.

1 0.3	**2** 0.19	**3** 0.27
4 0.81	**5** 0.99	**6** 0.03
7 0.07	**8** 0.01	**9** 0.123
10 0.361	**11** 0.729	**12** 0.887
13 0.013	**14** 0.061	**15** 0.011
16 0.039	**17** 0.087	**18** 0.009
19 0.007	**20** 0.001	

In many cases the common fraction will have to be written in its simplest form. This is done by 'cancelling'.

Example 9

Turn these decimals into fractions.

a 0.4 **b** 0.08 **c** 0.375

a $0.4 = \frac{4}{10} = \frac{\cancel{4}^{2}}{\cancel{10}_{5}} = \frac{2}{5}$ (cancelling by 2)

b $0.08 = \frac{0}{10} + \frac{8}{100} = \frac{8}{100} = \frac{8 \div 4}{100 \div 4} = \frac{2}{25}$

c $0.375 = \frac{3}{10} + \frac{7}{100} + \frac{5}{1000}$

$= \frac{300}{1000} + \frac{70}{1000} + \frac{5}{1000}$

$= \frac{375}{1000}$

$= \frac{375 \div 125}{1000 \div 125} = \frac{3}{8}$

Exercise 4.10

Turn these decimals into fractions.

1 0.8	**2** 0.45	**3** 0.55
4 0.85	**5** 0.14	**6** 0.22
7 0.46	**8** 0.82	**9** 0.38
10 0.98	**11** 0.32	**12** 0.12
13 0.44	**14** 0.64	**15** 0.72
16 0.56	**17** 0.174	**18** 0.225
19 0.475	**20** 0.275	**21** 0.075
22 0.025	**23** 0.012	**24** 0.016
25 0.088	**26** 0.006	**27** 0.008
28 0.005	**29** 0.002	**30** 0.004

Example 10

Find the sum of $\frac{1}{2}$ and 0.6.

Give your answer as a decimal.

$$\frac{1}{2} = 0.5$$

So $\quad \frac{1}{2} + 0.6 = 0.5 + 0.6 = 1.1$

Exercise 4.11

Find the sum of each of the following.

Give your answer as a decimal.

1 $\frac{1}{2}$ and 0.3   **2** $\frac{1}{2}$ and 0.9

3 $\frac{1}{4}$ and 0.45   **4** $\frac{1}{4}$ and 0.15

5 $\frac{3}{4}$ and 0.35

Find the difference between each of the following.

Give your answer as a decimal.

6 $\frac{1}{2}$ and 0.3   **7** $\frac{1}{4}$ and 0.05

8 $\frac{3}{4}$ and 0.15   **9** 0.95 and $\frac{3}{4}$

10 0.55 and $\frac{1}{4}$

Find the 'odd answer out' for the following.

11 a $\frac{1}{2} + 0.1$ **12 a** $\frac{1}{2} + 0.4$
     b $\frac{1}{4} + 0.35$ **b** $\frac{1}{4} + 0.55$
     c $\frac{3}{4} + 0.05$ **c** $\frac{3}{4} + 0.15$

13 a $\frac{1}{2} + 0.8$ **14 a** $\frac{1}{2} + 0.7$
     b $\frac{1}{4} + 0.85$ **b** $\frac{1}{4} + 0.95$
     c $\frac{3}{4} + 0.55$ **c** $\frac{3}{4} + 0.25$

15 a $\frac{1}{2} - 0.3$ **16 a** $\frac{1}{2} - 0.2$
     b $\frac{1}{4} - 0.05$ **b** $\frac{3}{4} - 0.35$
     c $\frac{3}{4} - 0.65$ **c** $0.65 - \frac{1}{4}$

17 a $\frac{1}{2} - 0.1$ **18 a** $0.7 - \frac{1}{2}$
     b $\frac{3}{4} - 0.45$ **b** $0.45 - \frac{1}{4}$
     c $0.9 - \frac{1}{2}$ **c** $\frac{1}{4} - 0.15$

19 a $\frac{3}{4} - 0.15$ **20 a** $\frac{1}{2} + 0.3$
     b $0.95 - \frac{1}{4}$ **b** $\frac{1}{4} + 0.65$
     c $\frac{1}{2} + 0.2$ **c** $1\frac{1}{4} - 0.45$

21 a $1\frac{1}{2} - 0.3$ **22 a** $1\frac{1}{4} + 0.35$
     b $1\frac{1}{4} + 0.15$ **b** $1\frac{3}{4} - 0.15$
     c $\frac{1}{2} + 0.9$ **c** $1.95 - \frac{1}{4}$

23 a $1.9 - \frac{1}{2}$ **24 a** $1.35 + \frac{1}{4}$
     b $0.85 + \frac{3}{4}$ **b** $2.3 - \frac{1}{2}$
     c $1.65 - \frac{1}{4}$ **c** $1.05 + \frac{3}{4}$

25 a $1.3 + \frac{1}{2}$ **26 a** $3.6 - 1\frac{1}{2}$
     b $1.15 + \frac{3}{4}$ **b** $2.85 - \frac{3}{4}$
     c $0.65 + 1\frac{1}{4}$ **c** $3.15 - 1\frac{1}{4}$

Fractions, percentages and decimals

A percentage is a special form of decimal. A percentage always indicates the number of *hundredths* in a share of a given quantity. The special sign '%' is used for a percentage.

This diagram shows the relationship between percentages, fractions and decimals.

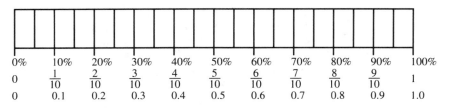

For example, if Surbajit was absent on 15% of the days during a school year, this means he was absent for:

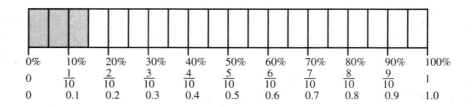

$$\frac{15}{100} = \begin{cases} 0.15 \\ \frac{3}{20} \text{ of the days.} \end{cases}$$

Example 11

Write the following as fractions and decimals.

a 57%   **b** 18%   **c** 35%

a $57\% = \frac{57}{100} = \begin{cases} 0.57 \text{ (as a decimal)} \\ \frac{57}{100} \text{ (as a fraction)} \end{cases}$

b $18\% = \frac{18}{100} = \begin{cases} 0.18 \text{ (as a decimal)} \\ \frac{9}{50} \text{ (as a fraction)} \end{cases}$

c $35\% = \frac{35}{100} = \begin{cases} 0.35 \text{ (as a decimal)} \\ \frac{7}{20} \text{ (as a fraction)} \end{cases}$

Exercise 4.12

Write the following as fractions and decimals.

1 63%	**2** 29%	**3** 13%	**4** 43%	**5** 77%
6 9%	**7** 22%	**8** 46%	**9** 82%	**10** 14%
11 34%	**12** 98%	**13** 58%	**14** 55%	**15** 85%
16 15%	**17** 5%	**18** 48%	**19** 64%	**20** 72%
21 84%	**22** 36%	**23** 28%	**24** 12%	**25** 8%
26 30%	**27** 10%	**28** 60%	**29** 40%	**30** 25%

We already know how to turn a decimal into a fraction.
To change a decimal into a percentage, multiply by 100%.

Example 12

Write the following as fractions and percentages.

a 0.7   b 0.07   c 0.64

a $0.7 = \frac{7}{10}$

   $0.7 = 0.7 \times 100\% = 70\%$

b $0.07 = \frac{7}{100}$

   $0.07 = 0.07 \times 100\% = 7\%$

c $0.64 = \frac{64}{100} = \frac{16}{25}$

   $0.64 = 0.64 \times 100\% = 64\%$

Exercise 4.13

Write the following as fractions and percentages.

1 0.5	**2** 0.31	**3** 0.4	**4** 0.04	**5** 0.8
6 0.08	**7** 0.9	**8** 0.09	**9** 0.05	**10** 0.23
11 0.32	**12** 0.99	**13** 0.1	**14** 0.01	**15** 0.75
16 0.29	**17** 0.92	**18** 0.02	**19** 0.2	**20** 19

We already know how to turn a fraction into a decimal and a decimal into
a percentage.
So we can change any fraction into a decimal and then into a percentage.

Example 13

Write the following as decimals and percentages.

a $\frac{11}{100}$ b $\frac{9}{10}$ c $\frac{3}{8}$

a $\frac{11}{100} = 0.11 = 0.11 \times 100\% = 11\%$

b $\frac{9}{10} = 0.9 = 0.9 \times 100\% = 90\%$

c $\frac{3}{8} = 0.325 = 0.325 \times 100\% = 32.5\%$

Exercise 4.14

Write the following as decimals and percentages.

1 $\frac{31}{100}$	**2** $\frac{27}{100}$	**3** $\frac{87}{100}$	**4** $\frac{99}{100}$	**5** $\frac{3}{100}$
6 $\frac{1}{100}$	**7** $\frac{9}{50}$	**8** $\frac{21}{50}$	**9** $\frac{19}{50}$	**10** $\frac{27}{50}$
11 $\frac{9}{20}$	**12** $\frac{13}{20}$	**13** $\frac{19}{20}$	**14** $\frac{4}{25}$	**15** $\frac{6}{25}$
16 $\frac{1}{25}$	**17** $\frac{8}{25}$	**18** $\frac{11}{25}$	**19** $\frac{13}{25}$	**20** $\frac{14}{25}$
21 $\frac{17}{25}$	**22** $\frac{7}{10}$	**23** $\frac{4}{5}$	**24** $\frac{3}{4}$	**25** $\frac{1}{2}$

Unit 5 Introducing algebra

1 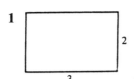 **2**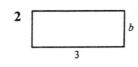

3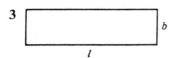

a area $= x \times y$
$\quad\quad\quad = xy$

b area $= 3 \times 2a$
$\quad\quad\quad = 3 \times 2 \times a$
$\quad\quad\quad = 6a$

c area $= 2a \times b$
$\quad\quad\quad = 2 \times a \times b$
$\quad\quad\quad = 2ab$

d area $= 3a \times 3a$
$\quad\quad\quad = 3 \times a \times 3 \times a$
$\quad\quad\quad = 3 \times 3 \times a \times a$
$\quad\quad\quad = 9a^2$

The area of rectangle **1** is 3×2

The area of rectangle **2** is $3 \times b$, usually written $3b$

The area of rectangle **3** is $l \times b$, usually written lb

4  **5**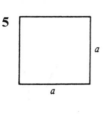

The area of square **4** is 3×3 or 3^2, read as 'three squared'

The area of square **5** is $a \times a$ or a^2, read as 'a squared'

Example 1

Find the area of the following.

a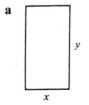

b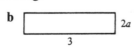

c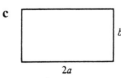

d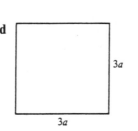

Exercise 5.1

Find the area of the following.

1    **2**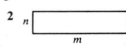

3 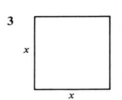   **4**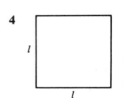

5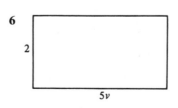

6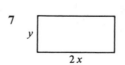

7

8

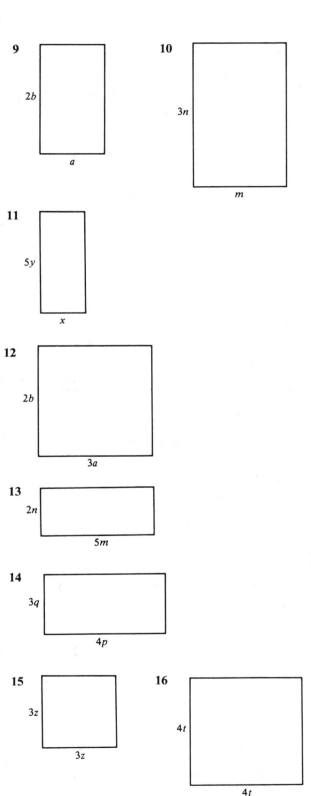

9 2b, a

10 3n, m

11 5y, x

12 2b, 3a

13 2n, 5m

14 3q, 4p

15 3z, 3z

16 4t, 4t

Example 2

In a bottle of medicine there are 30 doses. How many doses are there in

a 2 bottles
b 5 bottles
c x bottles
d $3a$ bottles?

In 1 bottle of medicine there are 30 doses.

a In 2 bottles of medicine there are
$30 \times 2 = 60$ doses

b In 5 bottles of medicine there are
$30 \times 5 = 150$ doses

c In x bottles of medicine there are
$30 \times x = 30x$ doses

d In $3a$ bottles of medicine there are
$30 \times 3a = 30 \times 3 \times a = 90a$ doses

Exercise 5.2

1 In a box of chalk there are 12 sticks of chalk.
How many sticks of chalk are there in
  a 2 boxes   **b** 5 boxes
  c x boxes   **d** $2x$ boxes?

2 In a book of stamps there are 10 stamps altogether.
How many stamps are there in
  a 3 books   **b** 6 books
  c x books   **d** $3x$ books?

3 In a match box there are 50 matches.
How many matches are there in
  a 2 boxes
  b 3 boxes
  c x boxes
  d $4x$ boxes?

4 A wrapped loaf of bread has 20 slices.
How many slices are there in
  a 3 loaves   **b** 5 loaves
  c y loaves   **d** $10y$ loaves?

5 A writing pad contains 40 sheets of paper.
How many sheets are there in
- **a** 2 pads
- **b** 5 pads
- **c** *y* pads
- **d** 5*y* pads?

6 A bottle contains 100 tablets.
How many tablets are there in
- **a** 3 bottles
- **b** 6 bottles
- **c** *x* bottles
- **d** 4*y* bottles?

7 In a box of chocolates there are 25 chocolates altogether.
How many chocolates are there in
- **a** 2 boxes
- **b** 3 boxes
- **c** *x* boxes
- **d** 2*y* boxes?

8 A milkman uses crates which each hold 15 bottles.
How many bottles can be placed in
- **a** 2 crates
- **b** 4 crates
- **c** *p* crates
- **d** 4*q* crates?

Example 3

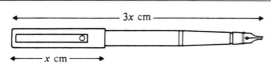

a What is the length of the pen top in millimetres?
b What is the length of the pen in millimetres?

In 1 cm there are $10 \times 1 \text{ mm} = 10 \text{ mm}$
In 2 cm there are $10 \times 2 \text{ mm} = 20 \text{ mm}$
In 5 cm there are $10 \times 5 \text{ mm} = 50 \text{ mm}$
In x cm there are $10 \times x \text{ mm} = 10x \text{ mm}$
In 3x cm there are $10 \times 3x \text{ mm}$
$$= 10 \times 3 \times x \text{ mm}$$
$$= 30x \text{ mm}$$

Answer **a** $10x$ mm
Answer **b** $30x$ mm

Exercise 5.3

1

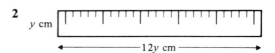

Find in millimetres
a the width, **b** the length
of the car number plate.

2

Find in millimetres
a the width, **b** the length
of the ruler.

3

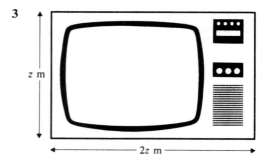

What is **a** the height, **b** the width
of the television in centimetres?

4 How many minutes are there in
- **a** 2 hours
- **b** 5 hours
- **c** *m* hours
- **d** 5*m* hours?

5 How many pence are there in
- **a** £5
- **b** £10
- **c** £*n*
- **d** £10*n*?

6 The outer dimensions of a picture frame are *a* cm long and *b* cm wide.
What is the perimeter in millimetres?

The expression for
3 more than 6 is $6 + 3$
3 more than x is $x + 3$
x more than 6 is $6 + x$
a more than 6 is $6 + a$
y more than x is $x + y$

The expression for
3 less than 6 is $6 - 3$
b less than 6 is $6 - b$
3 less than x is $x - 3$
a less than x is $x - a$

Exercise 5.4

Find the expression for each of the following.

1	5 more than x	**2**	5 more than y
3	2 more than a	**4**	x more than 4
5	p more than 3	**6**	t more than 2
7	x more than y	**8**	y more than x
9	p more than q	**10**	$2p$ more than 6
11	$3q$ more than 5	**12**	$4x$ more than 9
13	6 more than $5a$	**14**	8 more than $3b$
15	5 more than $7c$	**16**	$2b$ more than $3a$
17	$2y$ more than $5x$	**18**	$7q$ more than $4p$
19	5 less than x	**20**	5 less than y
21	2 less than a	**22**	x less than 4
23	p less than 3	**24**	t less than 2
25	x less than y	**26**	y less than x
27	p less than q	**28**	q less than p
29	6 less than $5a$	**30**	7 less than $2b$
31	4 less than $9c$	**32**	$2m$ less than 3
33	$5n$ less than 8	**34**	$3p$ less than 7
35	$9q$ less than 10	**36**	$2b$ less than $3a$
37	$8q$ less than $5p$	**38**	$4y$ less than $7x$
39	$3a$ less than $4b$	**40**	$2m$ less than $9n$

Substituting

$$5 + 5 = 2 \times 5$$

In the same way,

$$a + a = 2 \times a$$

usually written $2a$

and $x + x = 2 \times x$

usually written $2x$

and $b + b + b = 3 \times b$

usually written $3b$

But $a + a + b = (2 \times a) + b$
$$= 2a + b$$

Example 4

If $a = 4$, $b = 3$, $c = 2$, find the value of the following.

a $a + b$ **b** $b - c$

c $2a$ **d** $3c + a$

a $a + b = 4 + 3 = 7$

b $b - c = 3 - 2 = 1$

c $2a = 2 \times a = 2 \times 4 = 8$

d $3c + a = (3 \times c) + a$
$$= (3 \times 2) + 4$$
$$= 6 + 4$$
$$= 10$$

Exercise 5.5

Find the value of the following if $a = 4$, $b = 3$ and $c = 2$.

1	$a + b$	**2**	$2a$	**3**	$2a + b$
4	$a + c$	**5**	$2b$	**6**	$2a + c$
7	$b + c$	**8**	$2c$	**9**	$2b + c$
10	$b + a$	**11**	$3a$	**12**	$2b + a$
13	$c + b$	**14**	$4b$	**15**	$a + 3c$
16	$c + a$	**17**	$3c$	**18**	$b + 4a$
19	$a - b$	**20**	$4c$	**21**	$2c - b$
22	$b - c$	**23**	$5a$	**24**	$3c - a$
25	$a - c$	**26**	$6b$	**27**	$2b - a$
28	$a + b + c$	**29**	$4a$	**30**	$2c - a$

Find the value of the following if $x = 6$, $y = 5$ and $z = 2$.

31	$x + y$	**32**	$2x$	**33**	$3x + y$
34	$x - y$	**35**	$3y$	**36**	$2y + z$
37	$y + z$	**38**	$4z$	**39**	$4z + x$
40	$y - z$	**41**	$3x$	**42**	$3z + y$
43	$x + y + z$	**44**	$5y$	**45**	$5y + z$
46	$y + z - x$	**47**	$5z$	**48**	$4z - y$
49	$x + z - y$	**50**	$5x$	**51**	$3x - z$
52	$x - z + y$	**53**	$10z$	**54**	$7z - x$
55	$x + y - z$	**56**	$8y$	**57**	$3y - 2x$
58	$x - y + z$	**59**	$100y$	**60**	$5z - 2y$

$2 \times b$ is written $2b$

In the same way,

$3 \times b$ is written $3b$
$a \times b$ is written ab

Also,

$a \times b \times c = ab \times c = abc$
$2 \times a \times b = 2 \times ab = 2ab$

Example 5

If $a = 5$, $b = 4$, $c = 2$, $d = 0$, find the value of the following.

a $3a$ **b** ab **c** bcd **d** $2bc$

a $3a = 3 \times a = 3 \times 5 = 15$

b $ab = a \times b = 5 \times 4 = 20$

c $bcd = b \times c \times d$
$\qquad = 4 \times 2 \times 0$
$\qquad = 8 \times 0$
$\qquad = 0$

d $2bc = 2 \times b \times c$
$\qquad = 2 \times 4 \times 2$
$\qquad = 8 \times 2$
$\qquad = 16$

Exercise 5.6

Find the value of the following if $a = 4$, $b = 2$ and $c = 3$.

1 $3a$	**2** $7b$	**3** $5c$	**4** ab
5 $2ab$	**6** $3ab$	**7** bc	**8** $3bc$
9 $5bc$	**10** ac	**11** $4ac$	**12** abc

Find the value of the following if $p = 6$, $q = 4$, $r = 3$ and $s = 1$.

13 $3p$	**14** $6s$	**15** pq	**16** $5pq$
17 qr	**18** $2qr$	**19** pr	**20** $5pr$
21 rs	**22** $3rs$	**23** $4ps$	**24** $3qs$
25 pqr	**26** pqs	**27** prs	**28** qrs

Find the value of the following if $r = 6$, $s = 3$, $t = 2$ and $v = 0$

29 $5r$	**30** $7v$	**31** rs	**32** $2rs$
33 tv	**34** $5tv$	**35** $2st$	**36** ts
37 rt	**38** $4rt$	**39** $3rv$	**40** rst
41 tsr	**42** stv	**43** tvr	**44** vrs

$a \times a$ is *not* written aa

but $a \times a = a^2$ ('a squared')

$b \times b \times b$ is *not* written bbb

but $b \times b \times b = b^3$ ('b cubed')

Because $2a = 2 \times a$,

then $2a^2 = 2 \times a^2 = 2 \times a \times a$

Because $ab = a \times b$,

then $ab^2 = a \times b^2 = a \times b \times b$

Also $a^2b = a^2 \times b = a \times a \times b$

Example 6

If $a = 3$, $b = 2$, find the value of the following.

a a^2 **b** b^2 **c** a^3 **d** $2b^3$ **e** ab^2

a $a^2 = a \times a = 3 \times 3 = 9$

b $b^2 = b \times b = 2 \times 2 = 4$

c $a^3 = a \times a \times a$
$\qquad = 3 \times 3 \times 3$
$\qquad = 9 \times 3$
$\qquad = 27$

d $2b^3 = 2 \times b^3$
$\qquad = 2 \times b \times b \times b$
$\qquad = 2 \times 2 \times 2 \times 2$
$\qquad = 4 \times 2 \times 2$
$\qquad = 8 \times 2$
$\qquad = 16$

e $ab^2 = a \times b^2$
$\qquad = a \times b \times b$
$\qquad = 3 \times 2 \times 2$
$\qquad = 6 \times 2$
$\qquad = 12$

Exercise 5.7

Find the value of the following if $a = 2$ and $b = 3$.

1 a^2	**2** b^2	**3** $2a^2$	**4** $2b^2$	**5** $4a^2$
6 $3b^2$	**7** a^3	**8** b^3	**9** ab^2	**10** a^2b

Find the value of the following if $x = 4$ and $y = 1$.

11 x^2	**12** y^2	**13** $3x^2$	**14** $4y^2$	**15** $5x^2$
16 $10y^2$	**17** x^3	**18** y^3	**19** xy^2	**20** x^2y

Example 7

a If $y = mx + c$, find y when $m = 2$, $x = 3$ and $c = 1$.

b If $A = kr^2$, find A when $k = 3$ and $r = 2$.

a $y = mx + c$
$\quad = (mx) + c$
$\quad = (m \times x) + c$
$\quad = (2 \times 3) + 1$
$\quad = 6 + 1 = 7$

b $A = kr^2$
$\quad = k \times r \times r$
$\quad = 3 \times 2 \times 2$
$\quad = 6 \times 2 = 12$

Exercise 5.8

1 If $A = lb$, find A when $l = 3$, $b = 4$
2 If $A = bh$, find A when $b = 6$, $h = 5$
3 If $A = 6l^2$, find A when $l = 1$
4 If $y = mx + a$, find y when $m = 3$, $x = 2$, $a = 4$
5 If $z = nt - b$, find z when $n = 2$, $t = 5$, $b = 6$
6 If $p = c - lq$ find p when $c = 10$, $l = 2$, $q = 4$
7 If $P = 2l + 2b$, find P when $l = 8$, $b = 4$
8 If $S = 4l + 8b$, find S when $l = 5$, $b = 2$

9 If $D = \dfrac{m}{V}$, find D when $m = 104$, $V = 8$

10 If $t = \dfrac{3xy}{2z}$, find t when $x = 4$, $y = 5$, $z = 6$

Like terms

In the expression $3x + 4x - 5x$, there are *three terms*: $3x$, $4x$ and $5x$.

Terms such as $5x$, $4x$ and $3x$ are called *like terms*.
When connected by $+$ or $-$ signs, like terms can be collected together to give a single term.

Example 8

Collect together to give a single term.

a $5x + 3x$ **b** $4a - 3a$
c $8b + b - 9b$

a $5x + 3x = 8x$

b $4a - 3a = a$ (Note: this is not written $1a$)

c $8b + b - 9b = 0$ (Note: this is not written $0b$).

Exercise 5.9

Collect together to give a single term.

1 $a + a$	2 $b + b + b$
3 $c + c + c + c$	4 $d + d + d + d + d + d$
5 $l + 2l$	6 $m + 3m$
7 $n + 5n$	8 $3p + p$
9 $6q + q$	10 $8r + r$
11 $2t + 3t$	12 $3u + 5u$
13 $4v + 6v$	14 $5x + 2x$
15 $8y + 3y$	16 $3a + 6a + a$
17 $4b + 10b + b$	18 $5c + 6c + c$
19 $4m + m + 7m$	20 $n + 3n + 6n$
21 $2l + 3l + 7l$	22 $4p + 5p + 6p$
23 $6q + 7q + 7q$	24 $5a - 3a$
25 $7b - 4b$	26 $8c - 3c$

27 $10l - 4l$	28 $12m - 3m$
29 $4n - n$	30 $9p - p$
31 $12q - q$	32 $5r - 4r$
33 $8t - 7t$	34 $11u - 10u$
35 $2v - v$	36 $4a + 3a - 5a$
37 $6b + 2b - 3b$	38 $8c + 4c - 6c$
39 $7l + 4l - 5l$	40 $6m + 4m - 9m$
41 $5n + 2n - 7n$	42 $8p - 3p - 2p$
43 $9q - 4q - 3q$	44 $12r - 6r - 2r$
45 $7s - 2s - s$	46 $9t - 5t - t$
47 $8u - 5u - 2u$	48 $10v - 6v - 3v$
49 $7x - 5x - x$	50 $9y - 5y - 4y$

Remember that only like terms can be collected together to give a single term.

The expression $3x + 2y$ cannot be written as a single term.

The expression $4x^2 - 2x$ cannot be written as a single term.

Example 9

Collect like terms in the following:

a $3x + 4y + 2x$ **b** $x^2 + 4x + 2x^2 - 3x$

a $3x + 4y + 2x = 3x + 2x + 4y$
$\qquad\qquad\qquad\quad = 5x + 4y$

b $x^2 + 4x + 2x^2 - 3x = x^2 + 2x^2 + 4x - 3x$
$\qquad\qquad\qquad\qquad\qquad = 3x^2 + x$

Exercise 5.10

Collect like terms in the following.

1 $2x + 5y + 4x$	2 $3u + 7v + 5u$
3 $4a + 2b + 5a$	4 $6x + 4y + x$
5 $5m^2 + 3m + 2m^2$	6 $6n^2 + 8n + 3n^2$
7 $5u + 4v - 2u$	8 $7x + 9y - 5x$
9 $8p + 9q - p$	10 $4l + 7m - 3l$
11 $9z^2 + 4z - 6z^2$	12 $8a^2 + 6a - 3a^2$
13 $10b^2 + 5b - 2b^2$	14 $2m + 6n + 5m + 3n$
15 $3p + 7q + 2p + 5q$	16 $2u + 5v + u + 3v$
17 $3x^2 + 5x + 2x^2 + 4x$	18 $4y^2 + 7y + 3y^2 + 2y$
19 $2l + 7m + 3l - 4m$	20 $8b + 9c + 4b - 2c$
21 $5q + 9r + 2q - r$	22 $11a + 12b + a - b$
23 $6t^2 + 8t + 4t^2 - 5t$	24 $7u^2 + 9u + 5u^2 - 4u$
25 $7x + 5y - 4x + 2y$	26 $9a + 3b - 5a + 6b$
27 $8m + 5n - 7m + 3n$	28 $9p + 7q - 4p - 3q$
29 $10u + 8v - 4u - 3v$	30 $8z^2 + 6z - 5z^2 - 4z$
31 $2a + 3b + 3a + 4b + 4a$	32 $3x + 4y + 5x + 2y + x$
33 $8p + 6q - 3p - 2q + 4p$	
34 $15c + 12d - 8c - 9d - 3c$	

54

Indices

2^3 is read as 'two cubed'
$$2^3 = 2 \times 2 \times 2 = 8$$

5^2 is read as 'five squared'
$$5^2 = 5 \times 5 = 25$$

a^2 is read as 'a cubed'
$$a^3 = a \times a \times a$$

x^2 is read as 'x squared'
$$x^2 = x \times x$$

In the term 2^3, the figure 3 is called the *index* (plural 'indices').

Example 10

Find the value of the following.

a 4^3 **b** 7^2 **c** $2^3 \times 3^2$

a $4^3 = 4 \times 4 \times 4$
$\quad = 16 \times 4 = 64$

b $7^2 = 7 \times 7 = 49$

c $2^3 \times 3^2 = 2 \times 2 \times 2 \times 3 \times 3$
$\quad\quad\quad = 8 \times 9 = 72$

Exercise 5.11

Find the value of the following.

1 2^2	**2** 3^2	**3** 4^2
4 6^2	**5** 10^2	**6** 3^3
7 6^3	**8** 10^3	**9** 5^3
10 1^3	**11** $2^2 \times 2^2$	**12** $2^2 \times 2^3$
13 $2^3 \times 2^3$	**14** $2^3 \times 2$	**15** $2^2 \times 3^2$
16 $2^2 \times 5^2$	**17** $3^2 \times 3^2$	**18** $3^3 \times 3$
19 $3^3 \times 5$	**20** $3^2 \times 5^2$	**21** $3^2 \times 10^2$
22 $10^2 \times 10$	**23** $5^2 \times 5$	**24** $10^2 \times 10^2$
25 $5^2 \times 10^2$		

Example 11

Express the following in index form.

a $4 \times 4 \times 4$ **b** $x \times x \times x$
c $3 \times 3 \times 5 \times 5$

a $4 \times 4 \times 4 = 4^3$

b $x \times x \times x = x^3$

c $3 \times 3 \times 5 \times 5 = 3^2 \times 5^2$

Exercise 5.12

Express the following in index form.

1 8×8	**2** 7×7
3 9×9	**4** $6 \times 6 \times 6$
5 $8 \times 8 \times 8$	**6** $10 \times 10 \times 10$
7 $12 \times 12 \times 12$	**8** $a \times a$
9 $p \times p$	**10** $t \times t$
11 $b \times b \times b$	**12** $m \times m \times m$
13 $z \times z \times z$	**14** $2 \times 2 \times 4 \times 4$
15 $3 \times 3 \times 5 \times 5$	**16** $6 \times 6 \times 10 \times 10$
17 $2 \times 2 \times 2 \times 7 \times 7$	**18** $4 \times 4 \times 4 \times 9 \times 9$
19 $5 \times 5 \times 5 \times 6 \times 6$	**20** $2 \times 2 \times 5 \times 5 \times 5$
21 $8 \times 8 \times 9 \times 9 \times 9$	**22** $x \times x \times x \times y \times y$
23 $m \times m \times n \times n$	**24** $u \times u \times v \times v$
25 $a \times a \times a \times b \times b$	**26** $y \times y \times y \times z \times z$
27 $u \times u \times u \times v \times v$	**28** $m \times m \times n \times n \times n$
29 $p \times p \times q \times q \times q$	**30** $c \times c \times d \times d \times d$

Example 12

Simplify the following.

a $x^2 \times x$ **b** $2a \times 3a$ **c** $4b \times 3b^2$

a $x^2 \times x = x \times x \times x = x^3$

b $2a \times 3a = 2 \times a \times 3 \times a$
$\quad\quad\quad = 2 \times 3 \times a \times a$
$\quad\quad\quad = 6 \times a \times a$
$\quad\quad\quad = 6 \times a^2 = 6a^2$

c $4b \times 3b^2 = 4 \times b \times 3 \times b \times b$
$\quad\quad\quad = 4 \times 3 \times b \times b \times b$
$\quad\quad\quad = 12 \times b \times b \times b$
$\quad\quad\quad = 12 \times b^3 = 12b^3$

Exercise 5.13

Simplify the following.

1 $x^2 \times x$	**2** $y^2 \times y$	**3** $a \times a^2$
4 $b \times b^2$	**5** $3p \times 2p$	**6** $5q \times 4q$
7 $3r \times 3r$	**8** $6s \times s$	**9** $4x^2 \times x$
10 $7y^2 \times y$	**11** $a^2 \times 3a$	**12** $b^2 \times 9b$
13 $5m^2 \times 3m$	**14** $6n^2 \times 2n$	**15** $4t^2 \times 4t$
16 $2u^2 \times 3u$	**17** $3v^2 \times 8v$	**18** $4z \times 5z^2$
19 $3a \times 4a^2$	**20** $2b \times 7b^2$	**21** $6c \times 4c^2$
22 $(3p)^2$	**23** $(4q)^2$	**24** $(2x)^2$
25 $(10y)^2$		

$\square + 5 = 8$

Both sides of this statement are equal. To keep this so, 3 has to be placed in the box on the left-hand side.

$3 + 5 = 8$

Simple equations

Example 13

For the following, find the number that has to be placed in the box to keep both sides of the statement equal.

a $6 + \square = 10$ **b** $16 - \square = 10$
c $\square - 6 = 12$

a $6 + \square = 10$
  $\therefore \quad \square = 4$ because $6 + 4 = 10$

b $16 - \square = 10$
  $\therefore \quad \square = 6$ because $16 - 6 = 10$

c $\square - 6 = 12$
  $\therefore \quad \square = 18$ because $18 - 6 = 12$

Exercise 5.14

Find the number that has to be placed in the box to keep both sides equal.

1 $\square + 2 = 5$ **2** $\square + 4 = 6$ **3** $\square + 6 = 9$
4 $\square + 3 = 7$ **5** $\square + 7 = 9$ **6** $6 + \square = 8$
7 $2 + \square = 6$ **8** $4 + \square = 7$ **9** $3 + \square = 6$
10 $2 + \square = 9$ **11** $8 - \square = 6$ **12** $6 - \square = 2$
13 $7 - \square = 5$ **14** $5 - \square = 2$ **15** $8 - \square = 3$
16 $9 - \square = 6$ **17** $\square - 2 = 3$ **18** $\square - 3 = 5$
19 $\square - 4 = 2$ **20** $\square - 4 = 5$

$x + 4 = 10$

Both sides of this equation are equal. To keep this so, x has to be equal to 6 because

$6 + 4 = 10$

Example 14

Find the number that has to replace the letter to keep both sides equal.

a $x + 8 = 11$ **b** $a - 8 = 11$ **c** $11 - b = 3$

a $x + 8 = 11$
  $\therefore \quad x = 3$ because $3 + 8 = 11$

b $a - 8 = 11$
  $\therefore \quad a = 19$ because $19 - 8 = 11$

c $11 - b = 3$
  $\therefore \quad b = 8$ because $11 - 8 = 3$

Exercise 5.15

Find the number that has to replace the letter to keep both sides equal.

1 $x + 3 = 5$ **2** $x + 5 = 9$ **3** $x + 2 = 8$
4 $y + 3 = 9$ **5** $y + 4 = 8$ **6** $z + 2 = 4$
7 $a + 1 = 9$ **8** $b + 4 = 5$ **9** $c + 9 = 12$
10 $d + 4 = 10$ **11** $3 + x = 8$ **12** $5 + x = 7$
13 $4 + m = 9$ **14** $2 + n = 7$ **15** $1 + p = 8$
16 $8 + q = 9$ **17** $4 + r = 12$ **18** $7 + s = 10$
19 $9 + t = 11$ **20** $10 + u = 12$ **21** $8 - x = 5$
22 $6 - x = 4$ **23** $7 - y = 2$ **24** $9 - z = 7$
25 $8 - l = 2$ **26** $5 - u = 3$ **27** $9 - v = 4$
28 $4 - m = 2$ **29** $6 - n = 3$ **30** $9 - p = 8$
31 $10 - q = 6$ **32** $12 - r = 7$ **33** $x - 2 = 6$
34 $x - 4 = 3$ **35** $y - 3 = 2$ **36** $a - 2 = 4$
37 $b - 1 = 6$ **38** $c - 6 = 4$ **39** $d - 4 = 8$
40 $l - 1 = 9$

Example 15

a If $12x = 60$, find x.
b If $4a = 20$, find a.

a $\qquad 12x = 60$
  So $\quad 12 \times x = 60$
  $\therefore \qquad\qquad x = 5$ because $12 \times 5 = 60$

b $\qquad 4a = 20$
  So $\quad 4 \times a = 20$
  $\therefore \qquad\qquad a = 5$ because $4 \times 5 = 20$

Exercise 5.16

Find the value of the letter in each of the following.

1 $8x = 24$ **2** $7x = 35$ **3** $9a = 54$
4 $4b = 28$ **5** $6c = 48$ **6** $3l = 27$
7 $12m = 36$ **8** $2n = 40$ **9** $20p = 60$
10 $25q = 50$ **11** $30r = 90$ **12** $15t = 60$
13 $6a = 30$ **14** $8b = 32$ **15** $12c = 60$
16 $8l = 48$ **17** $12m = 48$ **18** $10n = 50$
19 $9p = 36$ **20** $12q = 108$

Example 16

Find the number that has to replace the letter to keep both sides equal.

a $4x + 6 = 14$ **b** $3a - 10 = 20$
c $6 - 2x = 0$

a $4x + 6 = 14$
So $4x = 8$ because $8 + 6 = 14$
∴ $x = 2$ because $4 \times 2 = 8$

b $3a - 10 = 20$
So $3a = 30$ because $30 - 10 = 20$
∴ $a = 10$ because $3 \times 10 = 30$

c $6 - 2x = 0$
So $2x = 6$ because $6 - 6 = 0$
∴ $x = 3$ because $2 \times 3 = 6$

Exercise 5.17

Find the number that has to replace the letter to keep both sides equal.

1	$2x + 3 = 9$	**2**	$2x + 4 = 12$
3	$2y + 1 = 13$	**4**	$2z + 6 = 8$
5	$3a + 2 = 8$	**6**	$3b + 4 = 16$
7	$3m + 3 = 18$	**8**	$3n + 7 = 10$
9	$4p + 3 = 15$	**10**	$4q + 2 = 10$
11	$4u + 4 = 20$	**12**	$5v + 6 = 16$
13	$5x + 9 = 14$	**14**	$2x - 3 = 5$
15	$2y - 4 = 2$	**16**	$2z - 7 = 3$
17	$2b - 1 = 11$	**18**	$2c - 8 = 0$
19	$3l - 5 = 7$	**20**	$3m - 6 = 9$
21	$4q - 3 = 5$	**22**	$4r - 8 = 12$
23	$5s - 1 = 14$	**24**	$6t - 2 = 10$
25	$9 - 2x = 3$	**26**	$12 - 2x = 4$
27	$10 - 2y = 0$	**28**	$8 - 3y = 2$
29	$10 - 3z = 1$	**30**	$18 - 5z = 3$

Exercise 5.18

For questions **1** to **8** find the 'odd answer out'.

1   **a** $x + 5 = 12$ **2**   **a** $y + 12 = 23$
    b $4x = 32$ **b** $7y = 84$
    c $x - 3 = 4$ **c** $y - 8 = 4$

3   **a** $15 + z = 24$ **4**   **a** $8 + t = 14$
    b $9z = 72$ **b** $20t = 120$
    c $11 - z = 3$ **c** $15 - t = 8$

5   **a** $4p + 3 = 15$ **6**   **a** $3q + 5 = 23$
    b $1 + 6p = 25$ **b** $6 + 2q = 16$
    c $7p - 5 = 16$ **c** $4q - 7 = 13$

7   **a** $8r + 7 = 55$ **8**   **a** $6x + 5 = 17$
    b $9 + 5r = 39$ **b** $4x - 9 = 3$
    c $9r - 13 = 50$ **c** $14 - 5x = 4$

For questions **9** to **18**, work out each value to find the 'odd answer out'.

9   If $a = 9$, $b = 6$ **10**   If $x = 6$, $y = 4$
    a $2a + b$ **a** $3x + y$
    b $4b$ **b** $5y$
    c $3a - b$ **c** $4x - y$

11   If $p = 2$, $q = 8$ **12**   If $m = 3$, $n = 4$
     a $3p + q$ **a** $m + 2n$
     b pq **b** mn
     c $12p - q$ **c** $5m - n$

13   If $u = 3$, $v = 2$ **14**   If $c = 2$, $d = 4$
     a $u + 3v$ **a** $c + 3d$
     b u^2 **b** $3c^2$
     c $4u - v$ **c** $9c - d$

15   If $a = 5$, $b = 3$ **16**   If $y = 3$, $z = 2$
     a $3a + 4b$ **a** $3y + 3z$
     b b^3 **b** $2z^3$
     c $6a - 2b$ **c** $10y - 7z$

17   If $m = 2$, $n = 4$ **18**   If $p = 4$, $q = 1$
     a $4m + 5n$ **a** $3p + 5q$
     b mn^2 **b** p^2
     c $20m - 3n$ **c** $5p - 4q$

For questions **19** to **21**, collect the like terms for each part to find the 'odd answer out'.

19   **a** $4x + 2y + 2x + 3y$ **20**   **a** $6p + 3q + 2p + 4q$
     b $5x + 7y + x - 2y$ **b** $3p + 9q + 5p - 3q$
     c $9x + 3y - 3x + y$ **c** $10p + 6q - 2p + q$

21   **a** $4m + 3n + 5m + 7n$
     b $2m + 11n + 6m - n$
     c $10m + 7n - 2m + 3n$

Unit 6   Metric units

Length

Measure the length of the pencil.

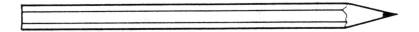

The length of an object like this is measured either in centimetres (cm), or in millimetres (mm).
The pencil is 10 cm long, or 100 mm long because

$$10 \, mm = 1 \, cm$$

Larger distances are measured in metres (m)

$$100 \, cm = 1 \, m$$

or in kilometres (km).

$$1000 \, m = 1 \, km$$

These are the four metric units in common use.

Exercise 6.1

In questions **1** to **7**, measure the length of the object shown, using the given units.

1 The key in centimetres.

2 The pair of compasses in centimetres.

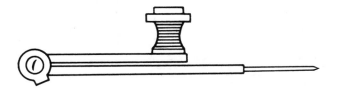

3 The screwdriver in centimetres.

4 The domino in cm and mm.

5 The match stick in mm.

6 The nail in mm.

7 The paper clip in mm.

8 Look at the car and trailer below.
Find the length of
  a the car   **b** the trailer
  c the car and trailer coupled together

9 Look at the bungalow below.
Find the width of
  a the bungalow and garage   **b** the garage only
  c the bungalow only   **d** the windows
  e the front door   **f** the garage door

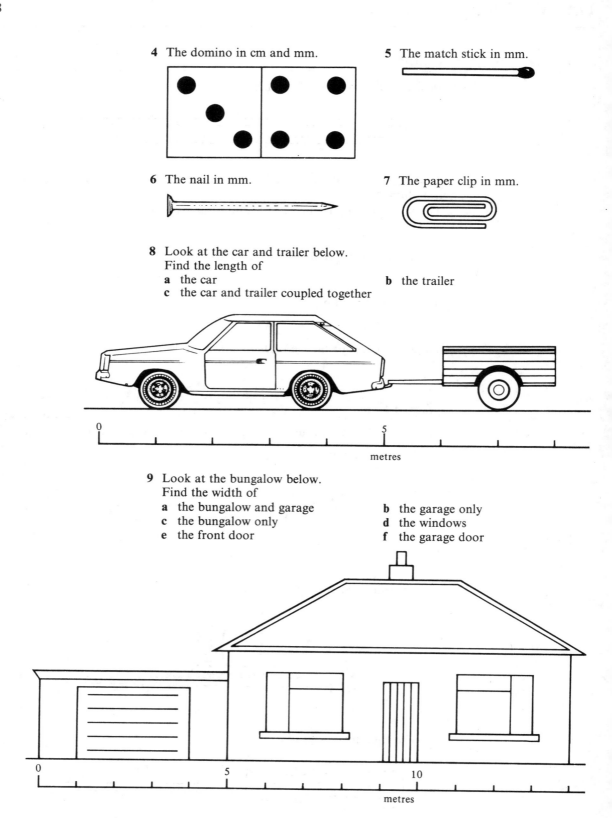

metres

metres

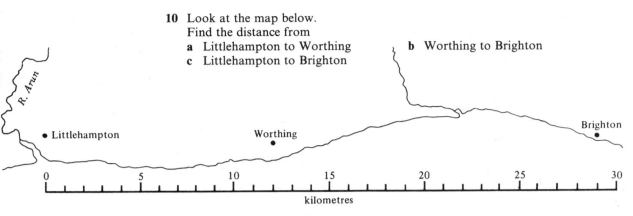

10 Look at the map below.
Find the distance from
a Littlehampton to Worthing   **b** Worthing to Brighton
c Littlehampton to Brighton

Example 1

a Change 160 millimetres (mm) to centimetres (cm).

b Change 4 kilometres (km) to metres (m).

c Change 275 centimetres (cm) to metres and centimetres.

a $160 \, mm = (160 \div 10) \, cm = 16 \, cm$

b $4 \, km = (4 \times 1000) \, m = 4000 \, m$

c $275 \, cm = (275 \div 100) \, m$
$= 2.75 \, m \text{ or } 2 \, m \, 75 \, cm$

Exercise 6.2

Change the following measurements into the units given.

1 7 cm, to mm	**2** 16 cm, to mm
3 28 cm, to mm	**4** 40 cm, to mm
5 190 mm, to cm	**6** 930 mm, to cm
7 60 mm, to cm	**8** 700 mm, to cm
9 8 m, to cm	**10** 45 m, to cm
11 236 m, to cm	**12** 320 m, to cm
13 500 m, to cm	**14** 30 m, to cm
15 7200 cm, to m	**16** 51 800 cm, to m
17 65 000 cm, to m	**18** 80 000 cm, to m
19 4000 cm, to m	**20** 4 km, to m
21 79 km, to m	**22** 137 km, to m
23 50 km, to m	**24** 290 km, to m
25 100 km, to m	**26** 42 000 m, to km
27 215 000 m, to km	**28** 80 000 m, to km
29 460 000 m, to km	**30** 300 000 m, to km
31 215 cm, to m and cm	**32** 632 cm, to m and cm
33 304 cm, to m and cm	**34** 1595 m, to km and m
35 4326 m, to km and m	**36** 2350 m, to km and m
37 3400 m, to km and m	**38** 5076 m, to km and m
39 54 mm, to cm and mm	**40** 79 mm, to cm and mm
41 8 cm 6 mm, to mm	**42** 9 cm 8 mm, to mm
43 1 m 45 cm, to cm	**44** 3 m 72 cm, to cm
45 5 m 7 cm, to cm	**46** 1 km 870 m, to m
47 2 km 356 m, to km	**48** 3 km 58 m, to m
49 4 km 80 m, to m	**50** 1 km 5 m, to m

Example 2

a Add together 3 mm, 5 mm and 8 mm. Give the answer in cm and mm.

b Find the sum of 4 cm 7 mm, 6 cm 3 mm and 2 cm 9 mm.

a $3 \, mm + 5 \, mm + 8 \, mm = 16 \, mm \text{ or } 1 \, cm \, 6 \, mm$

b

cm	mm	
4	7	
6	3	
+ 2	9	
13	9	Answer is 13 cm 9 mm

Exercise 6.3

Add the following.

1 2 mm, 8 mm, 9 mm	**2** 3 mm, 5 mm, 6 mm
3 9 mm, 6 mm, 8 mm	**4** 53 cm, 35 cm, 41 cm
5 46 cm, 37 cm, 63 cm	**6** 27 cm, 36 cm, 55 cm
7 334 m, 221 m, 713 m	**8** 403 m, 626 m, 545 m
9 824 m, 253 m, 65 m	**10** 953 m, 36 m, 75 m

Find the sum for each part of the question, then state which is the 'odd answer out'.

11 a 3 mm, 8 mm, 7 mm
   b 5 mm, 6 mm, 8 mm
   c 4 mm, 5 mm, 9 mm
   d 1 mm, 9 mm, 8 mm

12 **a** 5 mm, 4 mm, 7 mm, 8 mm
  b 3 mm, 9 mm, 5 mm, 6 mm
  c 8 mm, 4 mm, 4 mm, 7 mm
  d 2 mm, 9 mm, 8 mm, 4 mm

13 **a** 33 cm, 50 cm, 61 cm
  b 51 cm, 12 cm, 91 cm
  c 45 cm, 83 cm, 26 cm
  d 64 cm, 82 cm, 8 cm

14 **a** 25 cm, 31 cm, 20 cm, 53 cm
  b 42 cm, 12 cm, 71 cm, 4 cm
  c 35 cm, 17 cm, 64 cm, 23 cm
  d 50 cm, 37 cm, 13 cm, 29 cm

15 **a** 451 m, 332 m, 542 m
  b 270 m, 651 m, 404 m
  c 534 m, 705 m, 86 m
  d 217 m, 865 m, 233 m

16 **a** 173 m, 255 m, 232 m, 704 m
  b 206 m, 410 m, 587 m, 61 m
  c 429 m, 101 m, 303 m, 431 m
  d 317 m, 615 m, 30 m, 302 m

Find the sum for each question.

17 3 cm 5 mm, 2 cm 1 mm, 1 cm 3 mm
18 2 cm 3 mm, 4 cm 2 mm, 1 cm 7 mm
19 4 cm 6 mm, 1 cm 4 mm, 3 cm 5 mm
20 4 m 42 cm, 1 m 21 cm, 2 m 13 cm
21 3 m 45 cm, 1 m 16 cm, 5 m 23 cm
22 1 m 81 cm, 3 m 63 cm, 4 m 18 cm
23 2 km 235 m, 1 km 182 m, 5 km 335 m
24 3 km 416 m, 2 km 523 m, 3 km 345 m
25 1 km 504 m, 3 km 174 m, 2 km 667 m
26 1 km 525 m, 1 km 163 m, 1 km 368 m

Find the sum for each part of the question, then state which is the 'odd answer out'.

27 **a** 5 cm 1 mm, 2 cm 3 mm, 1 cm 2 mm
  b 2 cm 7 mm, 4 cm 3 mm, 1 cm 6 mm
  c 3 cm 5 mm, 2 cm 9 mm, 2 cm 3 mm
  d 5 cm 4 mm, 1 cm 8 mm, 1 cm 4 mm

28 **a** 4 cm 6 mm, 3 cm 5 mm, 1 cm 4 mm
  b 2 cm 3 mm, 1 cm 7 mm, 5 cm 6 mm
  c 3 cm 8 mm, 2 cm 7 mm, 3 cm
  d 6 cm 3 mm, 2 cm 4 mm, 8 mm

29 **a** 1 m 52 cm, 2 m 31 cm, 3 m 42 cm
  b 4 m 23 cm, 1 m 78 cm, 1 m 24 cm
  c 2 m 17 cm, 1 m 32 cm, 3 m 76 cm
  d 1 m 59 cm, 1 m 30 cm, 4 m 46 cm

30 **a** 2 m 68 cm, 1 m 76 cm, 4 m
  b 5 m 75 cm, 2 m 43 cm, 36 cm
  c 3 m 67 cm, 1 m 81 cm, 3 m 6 cm
  d 4 m 42 cm, 1 m 9 cm, 3 m 3 cm

31 **a** 2 km 542 m, 1 km 235 m, 3 km 473 m
  b 1 km 816 m, 1 km 334 m, 4 km
  c 2 km 257 m, 4 km 361 m, 532 m
  d 6 km 151 m, 913 m, 86 m

32 **a** 4 km 265 m, 3 km 113 m, 2 km 72 m
  b 5 km 394 m, 1 km 32 m, 3 km 24 m
  c 2 km 193 m, 2 km 151 m, 5 km 6 m
  d 1 km 364 m, 6 km 82 m, 2 km 4 m

Example 3

a Find the difference between 2 cm and 1 cm 4 mm.
b Subtract 2 cm 8 mm from 4 cm 2 mm.

a The difference is (2 cm) − (1 cm 4 mm)
  = 20 mm − 14 mm
  = 6 mm

b Set the subtraction out like this.

cm	mm
4	2
− 2	8
1	4

Answer is 1 cm 4 mm

Exercise 6.4

Find the difference between

1 5 cm and 4 cm 6 mm **2** 3 cm and 2 cm 7 mm
3 3 cm and 1 cm 4 mm **4** 5 cm and 1 cm 8 mm
5 4 m and 3 m 56 cm **6** 2 m and 1 m 72 cm
7 6 m and 2 m 35 cm **8** 5 m and 1 m 40 cm
9 8 m and 3 m 4 cm **10** 6 km and 5 km 750 m
11 5 km and 3 km 645 m **12** 7 km and 3 km 826 m
13 4 km and 2 km 68 m **14** 6 km and 2 km 40 m
15 6 km and 2 km 5 m **16** 9 km and 2 km 925 m

Subtract for each part of the question, then state which is the 'odd answer out'.

17 **a** 2 cm 3 mm from 5 cm 8 mm
  b 3 cm 7 mm from 7 cm 2 mm
  c 5 cm 9 mm from 9 cm 6 mm

18 **a** 6 cm 4 mm from 8 cm 9 mm
  b 1 cm 6 mm from 4 cm 3 mm
  c 7 cm from 9 cm 7 mm

19 **a** 6 m 54 cm from 9 m 79 cm
  b 2 m 47 cm from 5 m 82 cm
  c 5 m 35 cm from 8 m 60 cm

20 a 2 m 83 cm from 7 m 29 cm
b 1 m 91 cm from 6 m 27 cm
c 3 m 68 cm from 8 m 14 cm

21 a 1 m 8 cm from 3 m 63 cm
b 3 m 61 cm from 6 m 6 cm
c 2 m 5 cm from 4 m 60 cm

22 a 5 km 152 m from 7 km 487 m
b 3 km 328 m from 5 km 673 m
c 1 km 594 m from 3 km 939 m

23 a 3 km 716 m from 5 km 258 m
b 2 km 783 m from 4 km 425 m
c 1 km 589 m from 3 km 131 m

24 a 4 km 858 m from 7 km 320 m
b 1 km 738 m from 4 km 200 m
c 3 km 87 m from 5 km 539 m

25 a 3 km 7 m from 6 km 591 m
b 248 m from 3 km 822 m
c 683 m from 4 km 257 m

Example 4

What length of wood is needed to make this picture frame?

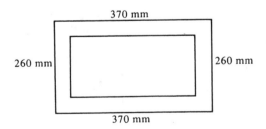

If the wood is only sold in one-metre lengths, how many lengths of wood must be bought?

What length of wood is left over?

Length needed = 260 + 370 + 260 + 370 mm
= 1260 mm
= 126 cm = 1 m 26 cm

So 2 lengths of wood must be bought.

The length of wood left over is

2 m − 1 m 26 cm = 200 cm − 126 cm = 74 cm

Exercise 6.5

1 What length of wood is needed to make this gate?

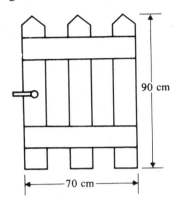

The wood is only sold in one-metre lengths.
How many lengths must be bought?
What length of wood is left over?

2 A woman buys a 5-metre length of curtain track for these two windows.

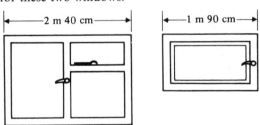

She cuts off 2 lengths to fit the windows.
What length of track will be left over?

3 A man has a 10-metre ball of string which he uses for fastening three parcels.

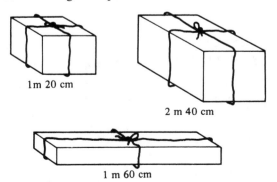

The lengths required are shown.
How much string will be left on the ball?

62

Mass

The units of mass which are commonly used are the gram, the kilogram and the tonne.

1000 grams (g)   = 1 kilogram (kg)
1000 kilograms (kg) = 1 tonne (t)

The gram is a very small mass.

A sugar lump
weighs about 5 g.

An apple weighs
about 100 g.

A full bottle of
milk weighs
about 1 kg.

A plastic bucket
full of water
weighs about 10 kg.

An electric cooker
weighs about 50 kg.

This weight is too
heavy for most
people to lift.

An ordinary car for
4 passengers weighs
about 2 t.

Look at the examples illustrated, then give the most sensible unit for measuring the weight of each of the following.

1 A cotton reel   2 A sack of potatoes
3 A ballpoint pen   4 A lorry
5 A light bulb   6 A television set
7 A large bunch of bananas
8 An aeroplane
9 A full bottle of ink
10 A bicycle

Example 5

Change the following as indicated.

a 3000 g, to kg   **b** 6 t, to kg
c 2 kg 625 g, to g

a 3000 = 3000 ÷ 1000 kg = 3 kg
b 6 t = 6 × 1000 kg = 6000 kg
c 2 kg 625 g = (2 × 1000) + 625 g
                            = 2625 g

Exercise 6.7

Change the following measurements into the units given.

1   5000 g, to kg   2   32 000 g, to kg
3   8 kg, to g   4   41 kg, to g
5   7000 kg, to t   6   96 000 kg, to t
7   9 t, to kg   8   80 t, to kg
9   2520 g, to kg and g   10   8075 g, to kg and g
11   4372 kg, to t and kg   12   5004 kg, to t and kg
13   3 kg 450 g, to g   14   5 kg 32 g, to g
15   6 t 321 kg, to kg   16   2 t 9 kg, to kg

Capacity

The units of capacity which are commonly used are the millilitre and the litre.

The millilitre is equivalent to the volume of a cube 1 cm by 1 cm by 1 cm, called a cubic centimetre.

1000 millilitres (ml) = 1 litre (l)

An Oxo cube has a volume of 8 ml

A can of cola has a volume of 330 ml

Bottles of lemonade come in 1 litre, 2 litre and 3 litre sizes.

Exercise 6.8

Give the most sensible unit for measuring the capacity of each of the following.

1 A fountain pen ink cartridge
2 A swimming pool
3 A fridge
4 A bottle of perfume
5 A can of paint
6 A car's petrol tank
7 A hypodermic syringe
8 A hot air balloon
9 A tea cup
10 A garden watering can.

Example 6

Change the following measurements into the units given.

a 4500 ml, to litres   **b** 3.45 litres, to ml

a 4500 ÷ 1000 = 4.5 litres

b 3.45 × 1000 = 3450 ml

Exercise 6.9

Change the following measurements into the units given.

1 5000 ml, to litres
2 3200 ml, to litres
3 6780 ml, to litres
4 5555 ml, to litres
5 345 ml, to litres
6 8 litres, to ml
7 17 litres, to ml
8 2.3 litres, to ml
9 3.45 litres, to ml
10 0.934 litres, to ml

Exercise 6.10

1 There are 35 English books in the pile on teacher's desk.
   If each book is 8 mm thick, what is the height of the pile
   a in millimetres   **b** in centimetres?

2 What is the distance between the wall and the gatepost shown in the picture below
   a in centimetres   **b** in metres?

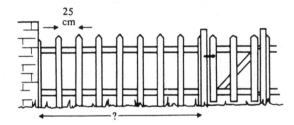

3 The picture shows a path made from paving stones that runs alongside a garage.

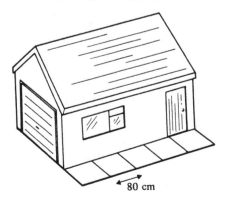

What is the length of the garage
a in centimetres   **b** in metres?

4 Larch Avenue is 874 m long. Beech Avenue is 345 m long. Elm Avenue is 781 m long.

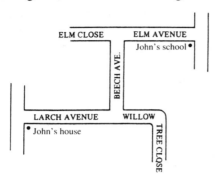

How far does John walk to school
a in metres **b** in kilometres?

5 Mrs Patel buys the following at the supermarket:
A packet of butter which weighs 250 g
A piece of cheese which weighs 450 g
A jar of jam which weighs 520 g
A packet of soap powder weighing 810 g
A bunch of bananas which weighs 690 g
If her empty shopping bag weighs 280 g, what is the total weight that she carries home
a in grams **b** in kilograms?

6 A cardboard case contains 24 cans of lemonade, each of weight 325 g.
If the empty case weighs 200 g, what is the weight of the full case
a in grams **b** in kilograms?

7 A man who weighs 80 kg loads 12 crates, each of weight 55 kg, on to a trolley of weight 260 kg.
He then pushes the full trolley into a lift cage where there is a notice as follows:

Load not to exceed 1 tonne

Is it safe to start the lift?

8 Twelve coloured pencils, each of weight 8 g, are contained in a cardboard packet of weight 29 g.
a What is the weight of the full packet?
b How many of the same packets would together weigh 1 kg?

9 A cardboard box of weight 34 g contains six golf balls.
If the box and the balls weigh 250 g altogether, what is the weight of one golf ball?

10 A chocolate Easter egg contains twenty-five chocolate drops. The chocolate shell weighing 113 g is wrapped in a decorative pack that weighs 12 g.
If the total weight is 250 g, what is the weight of each chocolate drop?

11 Mrs Jones buys a bag of flour containing 400 g.
If she uses 150 g for making some scones and 165 g for making a pie, how much flour will she have left over?

12 The total weight of a van and its load is 5 tonnes.
If the van carries 10 crates, each having a weight of 270 kg, find the weight of the van when empty.

13 To make a fruit punch for a party, Tammy mixes three 1 litre boxes of orange juice with two 1 litre boxes of pineapple juice and ten 500 ml bottles of lemonade.

What is the total volume of the fruit punch?

14 A pack of twelve cans of drink contains a total volume of 3.96 litres.
a What volume of drink is contained in each can?
b What volume of drink would be contained in a pack of 6 of the cans?

15 A large coffee urn contains 15 litres of tea and is used to fill cups with 125 ml of tea in each.

a How many cups can be filled from a full urn of tea?
b If 40 cups have been filled from a full urn, what volume of tea is left in the urn?

Converting Imperial to metric

Britain started using metric measurements during the 1970s. Until that time length, mass and capacity were measured using *Imperial* units.

The Imperial table for length is

$$12 \text{ inches} = 1 \text{ foot}$$
$$3 \text{ feet} = 1 \text{ yard}$$
$$1760 \text{ yards} = 1 \text{ mile}$$

One inch is approximately 2.5 centimetres.

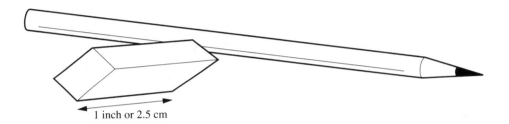

1 inch or 2.5 cm

A yard is slightly shorter than a metre.

A kilometre is approximately $\frac{5}{8}$ of a mile. This is more easily remembered as

$$8 \text{ kilometres} = 5 \text{ miles}$$

Example 7

a This pencil is approximately 6 inches long.

What is the length of the pencil in centimetres?

b A family see this sign while driving in France.

How far is it in miles to Paris?

a The pencil is approximately $6 \times 2.5 = 15\,\text{cm}$ long

b It is $160 \div 8 \times 5 = 100$ miles to Paris

Exercise 6.11

Find the approximate length of each object in centimetres.

1 Screwdriver

8 inches

2 Key

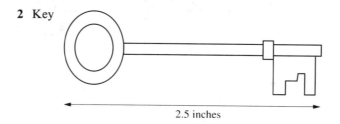

2.5 inches

3 Shoe

12 inches

4 Computer keyboard

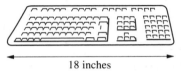

18 inches

5 Briefcase

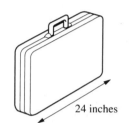

24 inches

6 Music keyboard

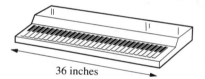

36 inches

7 Bed

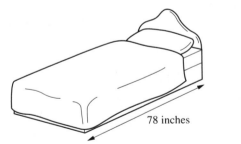

78 inches

8 Car

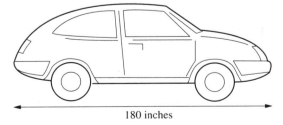

180 inches

Convert the distance shown on each sign into miles (to the nearest mile).

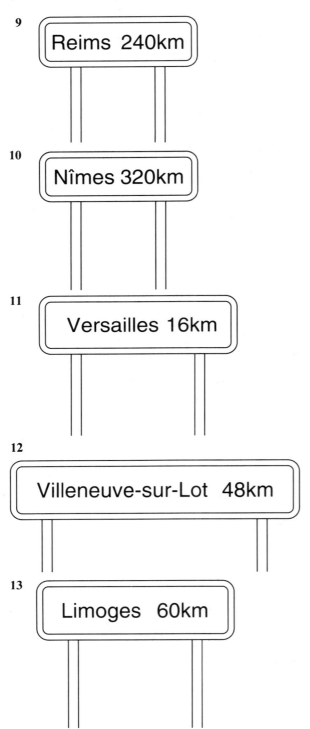

9 Reims 240km

10 Nîmes 320km

11 Versailles 16km

12 Villeneuve-sur-Lot 48km

13 Limoges 60km

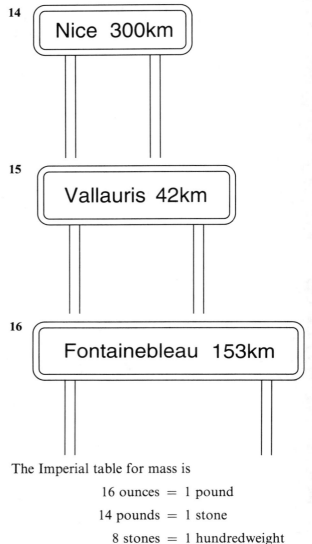

14 Nice 300km

15 Vallauris 42km

16 Fontainebleau 153km

The Imperial table for mass is

$$16 \text{ ounces} = 1 \text{ pound}$$
$$14 \text{ pounds} = 1 \text{ stone}$$
$$8 \text{ stones} = 1 \text{ hundredweight}$$
$$20 \text{ hundredweight} = 1 \text{ ton}$$

A kilogram is approximately 2.2 pounds.

Granulated SUGAR 1 kilogram

Granulated SUGAR 2.2 pounds

The imperial table for capacity is

8 pints = 1 gallon

A litre is approximately 1.75 pints.

1 pint   1 litre

Example 8

a Mr Wilson has just bought an 11 pound packet of grass seed.

How many kilograms of grass seed has Mr Wilson bought?

$11 \div 2.2 = 5$

Mr Wilson has bought 5 kg of grass seed.

b Mrs Wilson has just put 40 litres of petrol in her car.

How many gallons of petrol has Mrs Wilson put in her car?

$40 \times 1.75 = 70$

so 40 litres = 70 pints.

$70 \div 8 = 8.75$

So Mrs Wilson has put 8.75 gallons of petrol in her car.

Exercise 6.12

Copy and complete each weight label.

1

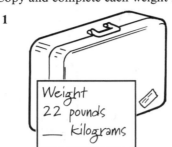

Weight
22 pounds
___ kilograms

2

Weight
44 pounds
___ kilograms

3

Weight
154 pounds
___ kilograms

4

Weight
330 pounds
___ kilograms

5

Weight
1430 pounds
_____ kilograms

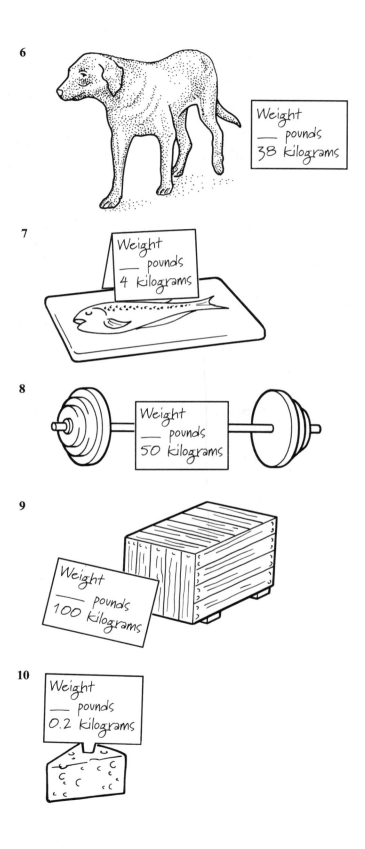

6

Weight
___ pounds
38 kilograms

7

Weight
___ pounds
4 kilograms

8

Weight
___ pounds
50 kilograms

9

Weight
___ pounds
100 kilograms

10

Weight
___ pounds
0.2 kilograms

How many pints of petrol are there in each can?

11

10 LITRES

12

15 LITRES

13

20 LITRES

14

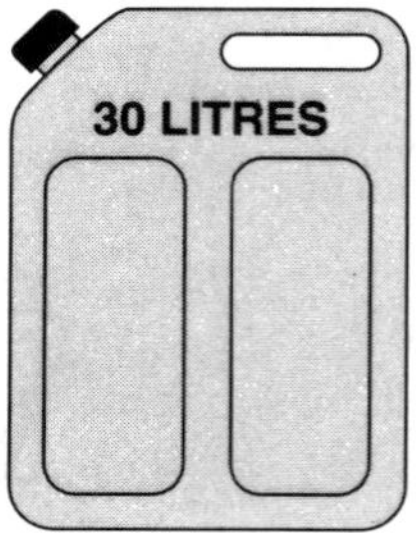

30 LITRES

15

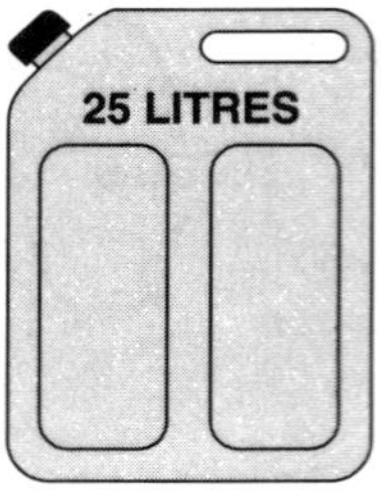

25 LITRES

How many gallons of petrol were there in each can in questions **11–15**?

Unit 7   Coordinates

Ordered pairs

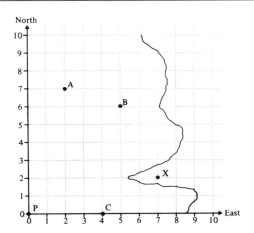

If you are standing at point P shown on the map the position of any other place on the map can be fixed by giving the following two distances

a the distance east of P
b the distance north of P.

On the above map, A is the point 2 km east of P and 7 km north of P. The position is usually given by the *ordered pair* (2, 7).

The ordered pair for the point B is (5, 6); the ordered pair for the point C is (4, 0). The order of the numbers is important. (7, 2) would give the point X and not the point A.

Exercise 7.1

1 Look at the places that are marked on the map, then copy and complete the details below.

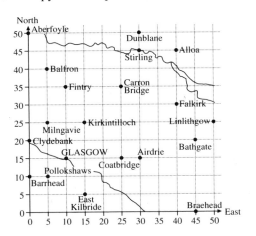

Barrhead (0, 10)
Clydebank (   )
Aberfoyle (   )
Pollokshaws (5, 10)
Milngavie (   )
Balfron (   )
Glasgow (10, 15)
Fintry (   )
East Kilbride (   )
Kirkintilloch (   )
Coatbridge (25, 15)
Carron Bridge (   )
Airdrie (   )
Stirling (   )
Dunblane (   )
Falkirk (   )
Alloa (   )
Braehead (   )
Bathgate (   )
Linlithgow (   )

2 Look at the theatre seats which have been reserved. Copy and complete the details below by giving the ordered pair for each child's seat.

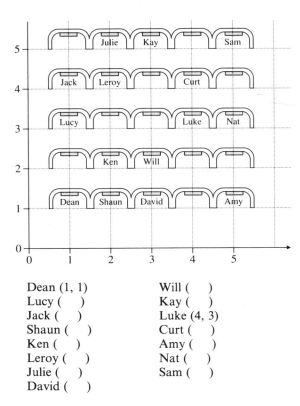

Dean (1, 1)   Will (   )
Lucy (   )   Kay (   )
Jack (   )   Luke (4, 3)
Shaun (   )   Curt (   )
Ken (   )   Amy (   )
Leroy (   )   Nat (   )
Julie (   )   Sam (   )
David (   )

3 Copy the map below and mark all the places whose ordered pairs are given

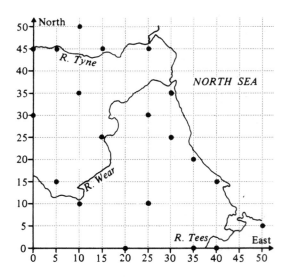

Consett (0, 30)
Sedgefield (25, 10)
Prudhoe (0, 45)
Houghton-le-Spring (25, 30)
Crook (5, 15)
Jarrow (25, 45)
Ryton (5, 45)
Easington Village (30, 25)
Bishop Auckland (10, 10)
Sunderland (30, 35)
Stanley (10, 35)
Stockton-on-Tees (35, 0)
Newcastle Airport (10, 50)
Blackhall Colliery (35, 20)
Durham (15, 25)
Middlesborough (40, 0)
Newcastle (15, 45)
Hartlepool (40, 15)
Coatham Mundeville (20, 0)
Redcar (50, 5)

The position of a point on a graph is fixed by referring to its ordered pair. The distances for each point along the axes are measured from a fixed point 0, called the origin.

The horizontal line from 0 is called the x-axis.
The vertical line from 0 is called the y-axis.

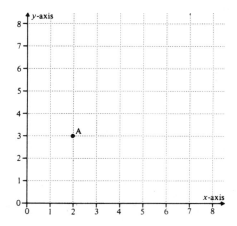

The position of any point given by the ordered pair (x, y) is the point which is x units to the 'east' of the origin and y units to the 'north' of the origin.
On the graph shown above, the ordered pair (2, 3) gives the position of the point A.

Example 1

Give the ordered pairs necessary to fix the position of each point shown in the diagram.

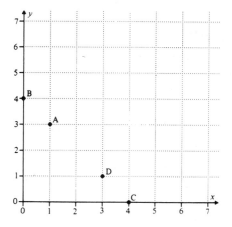

A is the point (1, 3)
B is the point (0, 4)
C is the point (4, 0)
D is the point (3, 1)

Exercise 7.2

Give the ordered pairs necessary to fix the position of each point shown in the diagram below.

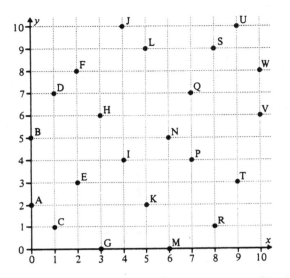

Example 2

On graph paper, with the *x*-axis numbered from 0 to 10 and the *y*-axis numbered from 0 to 8, plot the positions of the following points.

(1, 4), (1, 6), (3, 8), (5, 6), (5, 4), (7, 4), (7, 6), (9, 7), (10, 6), (9, 6), (9, 4), (8, 3), (8, 0), (7, 2), (5, 0), (5, 1), (3, 3), (3, 2), (1, 4)

Join each point to the next with a straight line. Then suggest a name for the picture you have drawn.

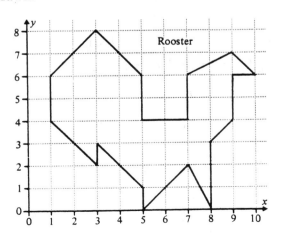

Rooster

Exercise 7.3

On graph paper, with the *x*-axis numbered from 0 to 10 and the *y*-axis numbered from 0 to 8, plot the positions of the points in each question.
Join each point to the next with a straight line.
Then suggest a name for the picture you have drawn.

1 (1, 2), (0, 4), (2, 4), (2, 5), (3, 5), (3, 6), (4, 6), (4, 5), (5, 5), (5, 6), (6, 6), (6, 5), (7, 5), (7, 4), (10, 4), (8, 2), (1, 2)

2 (5, 1), (5, 3), (0, 5), (0, 6), (5, 4), (5, 5), (10, 5), (10, 1), (5, 1)

3 (2, 0), (3, 1), (4, 1), (4, 4), (2, 4), (3, 8), (6, 8), (7, 4), (5, 4), (5, 1), (6, 1), (7, 0), (2, 0)

4 (2, 1), (3, 2), (4, 2), (4, 5), (0, 5), (0, 6), (4, 7), (4, 8), (5, 8), (5, 7), (9, 6), (9, 5), (5, 5), (5, 2), (6, 2), (7, 1), (5, 1), (5, 0), (4, 0), (4, 1), (2, 1)

5 (1, 4), (0, 4), (0, 7), (1, 7), (1, 6), (7, 6), (7, 7), (10, 7), (10, 4), (7, 4), (7, 5), (1, 5), (1, 4)

6 (1, 2), (1, 4), (0, 4), (0, 5), (7, 5), (8, 7), (9, 7), (10, 5), (10, 4), (9, 2), (8, 2), (7, 4), (3, 4), (3, 2), (1, 2)

7 (2, 3), (1, 3), (0, 4), (1, 4), (1, 5), (0, 5), (1, 6), (2, 6), (3, 5), (7, 5), (8, 6), (9, 6), (10, 5), (8, 5), (8, 4), (10, 4), (9, 3), (8, 3), (7, 4), (3, 4), (2, 3)

8 (5, 8), (8, 6), (10, 6), (10, 5), (8, 5), (5, 3), (10, 3), (10, 2), (5, 2), (8, 0), (6, 0), (3, 2), (1, 2), (1, 3), (3, 3), (6, 5), (1, 5), (1, 6), (6, 6), (3, 8), (5, 8)

For these two questions, use an *x*-axis numbered from 0 to 18 and a *y*-axis numbered from 0 to 18.

9 (11, 9), (11, 10), (10, 11), (8, 11), (7, 10), (7, 8), (8, 7), (9, 7), (9, 5), (10, 5), (14, 4), (17, 3), (18, 2), (18, 1), (17, 2), (14, 3), (10, 4), (8, 4), (4, 3), (1, 2), (0, 1), (0, 2), (1, 3), (4, 4), (8, 5), (9, 5)

10 (4, 18), (4, 17), (5, 17), (5, 16), (6, 16), (5, 15), (5, 14), (6, 14), (5, 13), (5, 12), (6, 12), (5, 11), (4, 11), (4, 3), (5, 2), (5, 0), (2, 0), (2, 2), (3, 3), (3, 11), (2, 11), (1, 12), (2, 12), (2, 13), (1, 14), (2, 14), (2, 15), (1, 16), (2, 16), (2, 17), (3, 17), (3, 18), (4, 18)

Straight lines

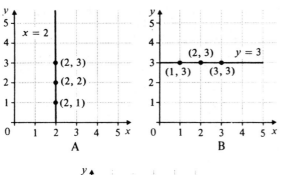

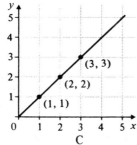

In graph A, all the ordered pairs which give points on the line have an x-value of 2; the line is the graph of $x = 2$.

In graph B, all the ordered pairs which give points on the line have a y-value of 3; the line is the graph of $y = 3$.

In graph C, all the ordered pairs which give points on the line have the x-value equal to the y-value; the line is the graph of $y = x$.

Example 3

Give the equation of the line for the graphs **a** and **b**.

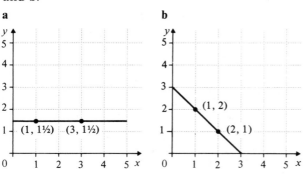

a As all the points on the line have a y-value of $1\frac{1}{2}$, the graph is $y = 1\frac{1}{2}$.

b As all the points on the line are such that the x-value added to the y-value equals 3, the graph is $x + y = 3$.

Exercise 7.4

Give the equation of the line for each of the following graphs.

1

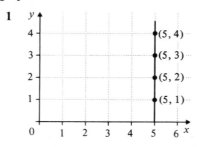

2

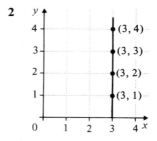

3

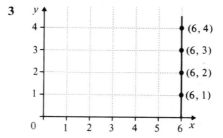

4

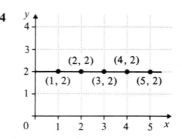

5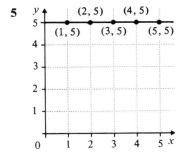

6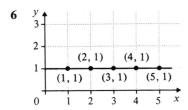

7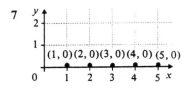

8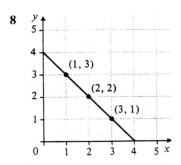

9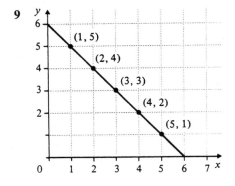

10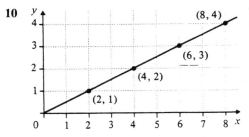

Draw the graphs of the following equations.

11	$x = 4$	**12**	$x = 1$	**13**	$x = 7$	**14**	$x = 0$
15	$y = 4$	**16**	$y = 6$	**17**	$y = 3$	**18**	$x + y = 5$
19	$x + y = 2$	**20**	$y = 3x$				

Sets of points

Some interesting results can be obtained when simple number properties are represented graphically.

Example 4

The table shows the pairs of numbers whose sum is 12.

1st number	0	1	2	3	4	5	6
2nd number	12	11	10	9	8	7	6

1st number	7	8	9	10	11	12
2nd number	5	4	3	2	1	0

Plot a graph of these numbers and join up the points with a suitable line.

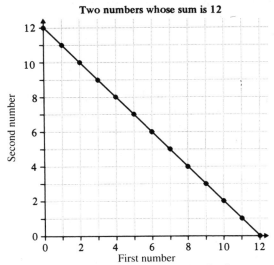

Two numbers whose sum is 12

The points can be joined by a straight line.

78

Example 5

The table shows the pairs of numbers whose product is 12.

1st number	1	2	3	4	6	12
2nd number	12	6	4	3	2	1

Plot a graph of these numbers and join up the points with a suitable line.

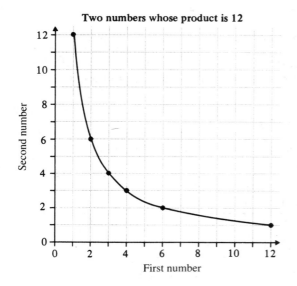

The points on this graph have to be joined by a smooth curve.

Exercise 7.5

1 The table below shows the pairs of numbers whose sum is 10.

1st number	0	1	2	3	4	5	6	7	8	9	10
2nd number	10	9	8	7	6	5	4	3	2	1	0

Using a scale of 1 cm to 1 unit on both axes, plot this graph.
Find from your graph what must be added
a to 3.6,   **b** to 8.2 in order to make 10.

2 The table below shows the pairs of numbers whose sum is 8.

1st number	0	1	2	3	4	5	6	7	8
2nd number	8	7	6	5	4	3	2	1	0

Using a scale of 1 cm to 1 unit on both axes, plot this graph.
Find from your graph what must be added
a to 6.8,   **b** to 0.4 in order to make 8.

3 The following table shows pairs of angles that add to 180°.

angle 1	0°	30°	60°	90°	120°	150°	180°
angle 2	180°	150°	120°	90°	60°	30°	0°

Using a scale of 1 cm to 10° on both axes, plot this graph.
Find from your graph the angle that would add to 180° with
a 24°   **b** 72°   **c** 144°   **d** 168°

4 The following table shows the change out of £1 for certain prices.

price (p)	20	40	60	80
change (p)	80	60	40	20

Using a scale of 1 cm to 10 p on both axes, plot the graph.
From the graph find the change out of £1 for the following prices
a 16 p   **b** 42 p   **c** 54 p   **d** 76 p

5 The table below shows the pairs of numbers whose product is 18.

1st number	1	2	3	6	9	18
2nd number	18	9	6	3	2	1

Using a scale of 1 cm to 1 unit on both axes, plot this graph.
Find from your graph by how much the following must be multiplied in order to make 18
a 3.6   **b** 15

6 The table below shows the pairs of numbers whose product is 16.

1st number	1	2	4	8	16
2nd number	16	8	4	2	1

Using a scale of 1 cm to 1 unit on both axes, plot this graph.
Find from your graph by how much the following must be multiplied in order to make 16
a 3.2   **b** 10

7 The following table shows certain pairs of numbers whose product is 180.

1st number	2	3	5	6	10	18	30	36	60	90
2nd number	90	60	36	30	18	10	6	5	3	2

Using a scale of 1 cm to 5 units on both axes, plot this graph.
Find from your graph what the second number is if the first number is
a 4 **b** 9 **c** 12

8 The following table shows the lengths and widths of certain rectangles which all have an area equal to 96 cm².

width (cm)	2	4	8	12	24	48
length (cm)	48	24	12	8	4	2

Using a scale of 1 cm to 5 cm on both axes, plot this graph.
Find from your graph the length of a rectangle of this same area if the width is equal to
a 3 cm **b** 6 cm

9 The table below shows the pairs of numbers less than ten whose difference is 2.

1st number	8	7	6	5	4	3	2
2nd number	6	5	4	3	2	1	0

Using a scale of 1 cm to 1 unit on both axes, plot this graph.

10 The table below shows the pairs of numbers less than ten whose ratio is 2.

1st number	8	6	4	2
2nd number	4	3	2	1

Plot this graph on the same axes as those used in question **9**, and hence find the pair of numbers which have both their difference and their ratio equal to 2.

11 a The table below shows the pairs of numbers less than ten whose difference is 3.

1st number	9	8	7	6	5	4	3
2nd number	6	5	4	3	2	1	0

Using a scale of 2 cm to 1 unit on both axes, plot this graph.

b The second table shows the pairs of numbers less than ten whose ratio is 3.

1st number	9	6	3
2nd number	3	2	1

Plot this information on the graph you completed in **a**.
Hence find the pair of numbers which have both their difference and their ratio equal to 3.
Express these two numbers in fractional form and in decimal form.

Straight line graphs

A graph compares two quantities. You will discover that the points given by these quantities on a graph often form a straight line; for example, distances on a map against real distances on land.

Example 6

The table below shows the real distance in kilometres and the map distance in centimetres between various towns.

real distance (km)	0	5	7.5	12.5
map distance (cm)	0	2	3	5

Using a scale of 1 cm to represent 2 km on the horizontal axis and a scale of 1 cm to represent 1 cm on the vertical axis, draw a suitable graph.

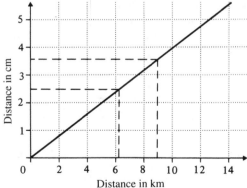
Real distance and map distance

From your graph, estimate

a the distance on the map between two towns which are 9 km apart
b the real distance between two towns when the map distance is 2.5 cm.

a Map distance is 3.6 cm
b Real distance is 6.3 km

Exercise 7.6

1 A flight of stairs reaches a height of 3 metres above the lower floor.
The table shows the height of certain stairs above the floor.

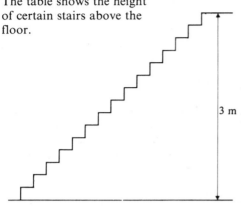

3 m

no. of stairs	2	4	5	10	13	15
height above floor (cm)	40	80	100	200	260	300

Draw a graph of the figures in the table using a horizontal scale of 1 cm to 1 stair and a vertical scale of 1 cm to 20 cm.

a Find from your graph the height above the floor of (i) the third stair, (ii) the seventh stair, (iii) the ninth stair, (iv) the eleventh stair.
b Find from your graph which stair I am standing on if my feet are (i) 120 cm, (ii) 160 cm, (iii) 240 cm, (iv) 280 cm above the lower floor.

2 The length of a spring is 10 cm. The spring is stretched by hanging weights from its end. The new lengths are given in the table.

weight (g)	0	10	15	30	45	60
length (cm)	10	12	13	16	19	22

Draw a graph of this information using a horizontal scale of 1 cm to 5 g and a vertical scale of 1 cm to 1 cm.

a Find from your graph the length of the spring when it supports a weight of (i) 5 g, (ii) 25 g, (iii) 40 g, (iv) 55 g.
b Find from your graph the weight required to stretch the spring to a length of (i) 14 cm, (ii) 17 cm, (iii) 20 cm.

3 The table shows the number of sheets of writing paper in a pile of a given height.

no. of sheets	100	250	350	500
height of pile (mm)	8	20	28	40

Draw a graph of this information using a horizontal scale of 1 cm to 50 sheets and a vertical scale of 1 cm to 2 mm.

a What is the height of a pile containing (i) 50 sheets, (ii) 150 sheets, (iii) 400 sheets?
b Find the number of sheets of paper in a pile of height (i) 16 mm, (ii) 24 mm, (iii) 36 mm.

4 The table gives the weight of each pile of writing paper listed in question 3.

no. of sheets	100	250	350	500
weight of pile (g)	400	1000	1400	2000

Display this information on a graph using a horizontal scale of 1 cm to 50 sheets and a vertical scale of 1 cm to 100 g.

a Use your graph to find the weight of a pile of (i) 50 sheets, (ii) 200 sheets, (iii) 300 sheets.
b What is the number of sheets in a pile weighing (i) 600 g, (ii) 1600 g, (iii) 1800 g?

5 The table shows the number of lumps of sugar of equal size contained in three different weights of packet.

weight of packet (g)	200	320	400	600
no. of lumps	60	96	120	180

Draw a graph to illustrate this information using a horizontal scale of 1 cm to 50 g and a vertical scale of 1 cm to 10 sugar lumps.

a How many sugar lumps could be contained in a packet weighing (i) 500 g, (ii) 560 g?
b Find the weight of a packet containing 144 lumps of sugar.

6 A girl produced this table of money equivalents for her Belgian pen friend.

British money	£1	£3	£4.50	£7	£8
Belgian francs	60	180	270	420	480

Plot a graph of this information using a horizontal scale of 2 cm to £1 and a vertical scale of 2 cm to 100 Belgian francs.

a From your graph find the value in Belgian francs of (i) 50 p, (ii) £2, (iii) £3.50, (iv) £7.50.
b What is the value in British money of (i) 150 Belgian francs, (ii) 240 Belgian francs, (iii) 390 Belgian francs?

7 The cost of a certain kind of curtain track is shown in the table.

length of window (cm)	80	100	140	200	250
cost of curtain track	48 p	60 p	84 p	£1.20	£1.50

Show this information on a graph using a horizontal scale of 1 cm to 10 cm and a vertical scale of 1 cm to 10 p.
What is the cost of curtain track for a window of length (i) 150 cm, (ii) 180 cm, (iii) 240 cm?

8 Six children are standing together in the sunshine. For some of the children the heights and shadow lengths are given in the table.

name	Aisha	Scott	Polly	Sanjay
height (cm)	100	120	132	160
shadow length (cm)	150	180	198	240

Using a scale of 1 cm to 10 cm on both axis, plot a graph of the above figures. (Use the horizontal axis for the heights.)
Find from your graph:
 (i) the length of Daniel's shadow if he is 140 cm tall,
 (ii) the length of Kelly's shadow if she is 108 cm tall.

9 Eight children have their photographs taken together. For some of the children, their real heights and their heights on the snapshot are given in the table.

name	Annie	Robert	Jason	Chantelle
real height (cm)	110	120	140	180
height on snapshot (mm)	55	60	70	90

Using a scale of 1 cm to 10 cm on the horizontal axis and a scale of 1 cm to 5 mm on the vertical axis, draw a graph of the above figures.
Find from your graph

a the height on the snapshot of (i) Melanie, who is 130 cm tall and (ii) Samita, who is 160 cm tall.

b the real height of (i) Jodie, who is 75 mm tall on the snapshot and (ii) Liam who is 85 mm tall on the snapshot.

10 The girls in class 4A have either auburn, blonde or dark hair. Details are given in the table.

colour of hair	auburn	blonde	dark
number of girls	2	6	12
percentage of girls	10%	30%	60%

Using a scale of 1 cm to 1 girl on the horizontal axis and a scale of 1 cm to 5% on the vertical axis draw a graph of the above figures.
Find the answers to the following from your graph
 (i) If 8 girls are hockey players what percentage of the class are hockey players?
 (ii) If 11 girls are netball players what percentage of the class are netball players?
 (iii) If 14 girls have blue eyes what percentage of the class have blue eyes?
 (iv) One day 15% of the girls arrive late. How many girls arrive late?
 (v) 25% of the girls cycle to school. What number of girls cycle to school?
 (vi) On a certain day 80% of the girls are present. What number of girls are present?

Unit 8   Averages

The average *height* of this group of children is found by adding together all their individual heights and dividing by the number of people in the group. There are 5 people, so divide by 5. Their average *weight* can be found in the same way. Find the sum of all their weights, and then divide by 5.

$$\text{average} = \frac{\text{sum of all the items}}{\text{total number of items}}$$

Example 1

Find the average of

a 6, 9 and 18
b £1.25, £2.75, £3.50 and £4.50

a $\text{average} = \dfrac{\text{sum of all the items}}{\text{total number of items}} = \dfrac{6 + 9 + 18}{3}$

$$= \frac{33}{3} = 11$$

b $\text{average} = \dfrac{\text{sum of all the items}}{\text{total number of items}}$

$$= \frac{£1.25 + £2.75 + £3.50 + £4.50}{4}$$

$$= \frac{£12}{4} = £3$$

Exercise 8.1

For questions **1** to **10**, find the average.
1 12, 13, 10, 9
2 10, 11, 7, 8
3 24, 28, 26, 22
4 99, 96, 87, 98

5 57 cm, 49 cm, 52 cm, 54 cm
6 71 kg, 68 kg, 81 kg, 73 kg, 82 kg
7 62 g, 56 g, 59 g, 64 g, 54 g
8 43 p, 51 p, 50 p, 47 p, 49 p
9 £33, £31, £32, £34, £30, £38
10 £3.10, £1.17, £2.16, £1.15, £3.19, £1.23
11 Over a six-week period a man's weekly wages were £173, £174, £181, £177, £171 and £174. Find his average wage.
12 Over a six-week period a newspaper girl's wages were £8.16, £7.75, £7.94, £8.10, £7.80 and £8.25. Find her average wage.
13 Mrs Robinson buys a kilogram of tomatoes on six different days. The prices that she pays are £1.15, £1.06, £1.04, 97 p, 93 p and 85 p. Find the average price.
14 A newspaper seller takes the following amounts of money during one week
Mon £31.40   Tue £30.50   Wed £30.20
Thur £33.10   Fri £32.60   Sat £40.20
Find his average daily takings.
15 The heights of four shrubs in a garden are 1 m 45 cm, 2 m 23 cm, 1 m 97 cm and 2 m 35 cm. Find the average height.
16 The head-to-tail lengths of four dogs are 1 m 13 cm, 1 m 8 cm, 95 cm and 84 cm. Find the average length.
17 Over a four-week period a woman's wages were £265.46, £275.38, £281.05 and £266.11. Find her average wage.
18 The ages of eight girls are 16, 11, 13, 10, 11, 12, 16 and 15 years. Find their average age.
19 The ages of eight boys are 13, 14, 11, 13, 10, 8, 9 and 10 years. Find their average age.
20 In eight innings a batsman makes the following scores: 35, 14, 15, 0, 37, 10, 6 and 3 runs. Find his average score.
21 There are twelve pupils in class 1A. Their marks out of 50 in an English test are 45, 46, 46, 47, 48, 49, 44, 47, 33, 35, 38 and 50. Find the average mark.
22 The weights of four cats are 9 kg 150 g, 8 kg 320 g, 8 kg 860 g, and 9 kg 670 g. Find their average weight.
23 The head-to-tail lengths of five white mice are 11 cm 7 mm, 12 cm 5 mm, 11 cm 9 mm, 13 cm 6 mm and 10 cm 3 mm. Find their average length.
24 The heights of five canaries are 10 cm 1 mm, 10 cm 9 mm, 9 cm 7 mm, 9 cm 5 mm and 9 cm 8 mm. Find their average height.

25 At Wood Lane Junior School there are five classes. The table shows how many boys and girls there are in each class.

	boys	girls
class 1	13	12
class 2	16	11
class 3	10	15
class 4	12	16
class 5	14	16

Find

a the average number of boys per class
b the average number of girls per class
c the total number of pupils in the school
d the average number of pupils per class.

Example 2

Find the average of the following.

a 16, 32, 41, 86, 97
b 1 m 40 cm, 2 m 52 cm, 4 m 22 cm, 1 m 8 cm

a average $= \dfrac{16 + 32 + 41 + 86 + 97}{5} = \dfrac{272}{5}$

$\qquad\qquad = 54\frac{2}{5}$ or 54.4

b average $= \dfrac{\begin{array}{c}1\,m\,40\,cm + 2\,m\,52\,cm + 4\,m\,22\,cm \\ + 1\,m\,8\,cm\end{array}}{4}$

$\qquad\qquad = \dfrac{9\,m\,22\,cm}{4} = \dfrac{922}{4}\ cm = 230.5\,cm$

Exercise 8.2

For questions **1** to **10**, find the average.

1 21, 15, 22, 20, 14
2 27, 30, 29, 28, 32
3 11 g, 13 g, 12 g, 9 g, 16 g, 20 g
4 £8, £9, £5, £12, £4, £7
5 32 kg, 20 kg, 10 kg, 8 kg, 5 kg, 12 kg, 13 kg, 16 kg
6 £15, £16, £13, £19, £20, £14, £12, £8, £9, £10
7 3, 0, 1, 2, 5, 3, 7, 4, 5, 6, 4, 2
8 6 m, 8 m, 7 m, 5 m, 11 m, 2 m
9 £2.25, £2.30, £2.15, £1.95, £2.15
10 £1.10, £1.04, 92 p, 89 p, £1
11 Find the average number of days per month in a leap year.

12 The heights of six men are 1 m 80 cm, 1 m 74 cm, 1 m 87 cm, 1 m 79 cm, 1 m 77 cm and 1 m 71 cm. Find their average height.
13 Over a five-week period a woman's weekly wages were £373, £382, £372, £378, £371. Find her average weekly wage.
14 An auctioneer sells five lambs at the following prices: £25, £28, £29, £26 and £30. Find the average selling price.
15 The lengths of six lettuce leaves are 20 cm 3 mm, 18 cm 6 mm, 16 cm 1 mm, 15 cm 8 mm, 16 cm 2 mm and 17 cm 4 mm. Find the average length of leaf.
16 The heights of six flowers in a window box are 14 cm 2 mm, 12 cm 7 mm, 11 cm 8 mm, 10 cm 6 mm, 9 cm 8 mm and 11 cm 1 mm. Find the average height.
17 The weights of five dogs are 21 kg 220 g, 22 kg 140 g, 20 kg 750 g, 20 kg 420 g and 23 kg 470 g. Find their average weight.
18 The capacities of three buckets are 9 *l* 450 ml, 10 *l* 260 ml and 10 *l* 140 ml. Find the average capacity.

The mean

The average you have been calculating is only one of a range of different types of average used in statistics.

Three averages are in common use, the *mean*, the *mode* and the *median*.

The average you have calculated is more correctly called the *mean average*.

Example 3

In ten boxes of matches, the number of matches was as follows.

$\qquad$ 37, 45, 41, 41, 42, 44, 39, 40, 41, 40

Find the mean number of matches per box.

The total number of matches is

$37 + 45 + 41 + 41 + 42 + 44 + 39 + 40 + 41 + 40$
$= 410$

The number of boxes $= 10$

So, mean number per box $= \dfrac{410}{10} = 41$

Exercise 8.3

1 Six boys have each bought one hundred grams of assorted sweets. The actual numbers of sweets that they have are

    19, 22, 20, 23, 20 and 22.

Find the mean number of sweets in a bag.

2 A theatre showed the same play for six nights of the same week. The attendances were

Mon 105	Wed 115	Fri 120
Tue 108	Thur 103	Sat 109

Find the mean attendance figure.

3 A hockey club won a trophy after a six-round contest. The scores in the matches were

1st round	5 3	3rd round 4 3	semi-final 3 2
2nd round	6 2	4th round 2 0	final 4 2

Find
  a the mean number of goals that they scored,
  b the mean number of goals that were scored against them.

4 Mrs Charlton had the following numbers of bottles of milk delivered during the course of a certain week.

Mon 4	Thur 4	Sat 2
Tue 4	Fri 2	Sun 1
Wed 4		

Find the mean number of bottles that she had per day.

5 The ages of the seven girls in a netball team are

    16, 19, 21, 18, 17, 17 and 18.

Find their mean age.

6 A taxi driver answers eight calls. The numbers of passengers that he carries are

    5, 4, 6, 3, 2, 6, 1 and 5

Find the mean number of passengers that he carries.

7 Eight similar bottles of pain-killing tablets have the following contents

    59, 62, 61, 57, 64, 63, 60 and 62 tablets.

Find the mean number of tablets per bottle.

8 A primary school has the following numbers of boys and girls in its four classes

class	boys	girls
1	12	13
2	11	8
3	14	12
4	15	11

Find
  a the mean number of boys per class,
  b the mean number of girls per class.

9 The list below shows how many hours a brick-layer worked on each day of a two-week period.

Mon	8	Mon	8
Tue	8	Tue	11
Wed	12	Wed	12
Thur	12	Thur	10
Fri	11	Fri	8

Find the mean number of hours per day that he worked.

10 Ten packets of paper clips had the following contents

    101, 102, 104, 108, 104, 102, 103, 107, 109, 110

Find the mean number of paper clips per packet.

11 Mr Chavda buys the following numbers of loaves of bread per week over a period of three months

    4, 3, 2, 2, 5, 4, 3, 2, 4, 1, 4, 2

Find the mean number of loaves per week that he buys.

12 A chicken lays the following numbers of eggs per week over a three-month period

    5, 2, 0, 1, 3, 2, 3, 1, 4, 0, 1, 2

Find the mean number of eggs laid per week.

13 Five train journeys from Buxton to Manchester took the following times

    57 min, 58 min, 55 min, 1 h 6 min and 1 h 4 min

Find the mean journey time.

14 Five bus journeys from Ludlow to Birmingham took the following times

    1 h 58 min, 1 h 56 min, 1 h 59 min, 1 h 57 min and 2 h 10 min

Find the mean journey time.

15 A football cup-tie had to be played three times because two matches ended as draws. The three attendance figures were

    52 804, 39 007, 45 760

Find the mean number of spectators per match.

The mode

The record that is 'Top of the Pops' is the most popular record sold during one week. It is therefore played more often than any other.

In any set of data, the *mode* or *modal average* is the most popular item, i.e. the item that is the most common.

The mode of a set of numbers is the one that occurs the most frequently.

Example 4

During one week the marks in Kate's English exercise book were

5, 7, 7, 9, 7

What was the modal mark?

The modal mark was 7 because this mark occurred more frequently than any other.

Example 5

The shoe sizes of a class of 20 pupils are as follows.

3, 5, 4, 5, 3, 3, 4, 4, 5, 7, 7, 4, 4, 4, 6, 7, 6, 7, 3, 5

Find the mode.

Tally chart

shoe size	tally	frequency
3	////	4
→ 4	⫲⫲⫲ /	6 ←
5	////	4
6	//	2
7	////	4
	total =	20

The most popular size is 4: this size is the one that occurs the most frequently.
So 4 is the mode.

Exercise 8.4

1 Twelve school pupils apply to go on an outward bound course. Their ages are

16, 14, 15, 16, 15, 17, 15, 16, 15, 17, 16, 15.

Find the mode of their ages.

2 The list below shows how many pupils in class 2B were absent on each day of a three-week period.

Mon	0	Mon	2	Mon	0
Tue	1	Tue	1	Tue	0
Wed	2	Wed	1	Wed	1
Thur	2	Thur	0	Thur	2
Fri	1	Fri	1	Fri	2

Find the modal number of absentees.

3 A cricketer plays for one club for fifteen seasons. The list below shows how many centuries that he scored in each of the seasons.

4, 3, 0, 5, 4, 5, 2, 4, 1, 2, 4, 1, 0, 2, 0

Find his modal number of centuries.

4 The list below shows how many suits were sold at a tailor's shop on each day of a three-week period.

Mon	2	Mon	1	Mon	4
Tue	1	Tue	4	Tue	1
Wed	4	Wed	3	Wed	5
Thur	2	Thur	2	Thur	3
Fri	3	Fri	5	Fri	2
Sat	5	Sat	2	Sat	4

Find the modal number of suits sold.

5 A dice is thrown twenty times and the scores are shown below.

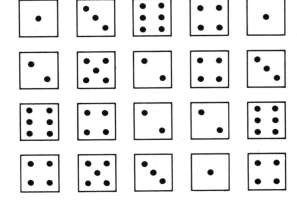

Find the modal score.

6 The list below shows how many lunches a cafe served on each day of a three-week period.

Mon	5	Mon	4	Mon	5
Tue	7	Tue	7	Tue	5
Wed	6	Wed	5	Wed	8
Thur	5	Thur	6	Thur	7
Fri	6	Fri	5	Fri	6
Sat	4	Sat	6	Sat	7

Find the modal number of lunches served.

7 A footballer made twenty appearances during a certain season and scored the following numbers of goals in the matches.

0, 1, 2, 1, 0, 2, 3, 0, 1, 2,
1, 0, 3, 0, 1, 2, 1, 3, 3, 2

Find the modal number of goals that he scored.

8 The list below shows how many pupils there are in each of the twenty classes at Westmead School.

26, 25, 24, 22, 24, 23, 26, 25, 23, 25,
26, 24, 25, 25, 22, 23, 23, 25, 24, 23

Find the modal number of pupils per class.

9 A tennis club has twenty-five members and the list below shows their ages.

16, 18, 15, 18, 16, 15, 14, 16, 17, 15, 17, 16, 17,
14, 18, 16, 18, 15, 18, 17, 17, 16, 17, 18, 17

Find the modal age of the members.

10 During a certain season a football team played in thirty matches and scored the following numbers of goals.

1, 0, 6, 2, 7, 2, 2, 3, 4, 3, 0, 6, 3, 2, 0,
1, 4, 3, 1, 5, 3, 0, 2, 1, 4, 0, 2, 6, 1, 5

Find the modal number of goals per match.

The median

If a number of items are arranged in order of size, the middle one of the items is the *median average*.

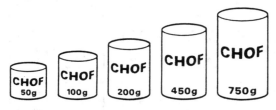

Look at the tins of dog food. The median size of tins of 'Chof' is 200 g.

Example 6

Two dice are thrown seven times. The results are as shown.

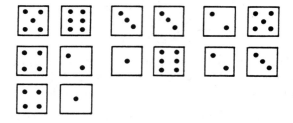

What is the median score?

The total scores are 11, 6, 7, 6, 7, 5, 5

When arranged in order of size, the list is

5, 5, 6, 6, 7, 7, 11

The middle figure is 6, so the median score is 6.

If there are an even number of items in a list, there will be no exact middle position. In this case, the median is found by taking the mean average of the two items on either side of the exact middle position.

Example 7

The rainfall (in mm) in a town is recorded each month. These are the results after one year.

20, 12, 15, 21, 12, 10, 5, 6, 12, 18, 21, 20

What is the median rainfall?

When arranged in order of size, the list is

5, 6, 10, 12, 12, 12, 15, 18, 20, 20, 21, 21

The median $= (12 + 15)/2 = 13.5\,\text{mm}$

Exercise 8.5

1 One week Peter goes to school by bus and finds that the bus arrives late by the following numbers of minutes

| Mon | 5 | Wed | 9 | Fri | 2 |
| Tue | 7 | Thur | 1 | | |

Find the median number of minutes late.

2 One week a travelling saleswoman calls at a garage every day and buys the following quantities of petrol

Mon	15 litres	Thur	24 litres
Tue	21 litres	Fri	12 litres
Wed	16 litres		

Find the median quantity that she buys.

3 A coach driver has to make five journeys from a railway station to a nearby holiday camp. The numbers of passengers that he carries are

36, 40, 33, 31, 25

Find the median number that he carries.

4 Mrs Andrews buys half a kilogram of tomatoes on six different occasions. The prices that she pays are

59 p, 62 p, 57 p, 61 p, 55 p, 58 p

Find the median price that she pays.

5 A rugby team wins a trophy after playing in a five-round contest. They win their matches by the following scores.

first round	24	10	semi-final	27 14
second round	9	6	final	19 4
third round	16	12		

Find
a the median number of points that they score,
b the median number of points that are scored against them.

6 The midday temperatures for a certain week during July were as follows.

Mon	22 °C	Thur	21 °C	Sat	26 °C
Tue	20 °C	Fri	23 °C	Sun	24 °C
Wed	19 °C				

Find the median temperature.

7 The list below shows how far I travel in my car on each day of a certain week.

Mon	42 km	Thur	61 km	Sat	35 km
Tue	53 km	Fri	94 km	Sun	90 km
Wed	47 km				

Find the median distance that I travel per day.

8 A train from Birmingham to Manchester makes six stops on the way. The list below shows the number of passengers in the train for each of the seven stages of the journey.

Birmingham to Wolverhampton	240
Wolverhampton to Stafford	200
Stafford to Stoke-on-Trent	230
Stoke-on-Trent to Congleton	190
Congleton to Macclesfield	180
Macclesfield to Stockport	210
Stockport to Manchester	170

Find the median number of passengers in the train.

9 A policeman who works at night found that in one year he required ten batteries for his bicycle headlamp. The times that they lasted were

42, 39, 36, 47, 51, 40, 44, 43, 33 and 32 days

Find the median time for which a battery lasted.

10 A cricket team were all out for 250 runs. The eleven players scored

65, 43, 35, 8, 21, 0, 6, 17, 32, 13 and 10 runs

Find their median score.

Mean, median and mode

Exercise 8.6

For each question find which of the mean, the median or the mode is different from the other two.

1 Tom travels to school by bus every day. One week he had to wait at the bus stop for the following times.

Monday	5 minutes	Thursday	5 minutes
Tuesday	9 minutes	Friday	4 minutes
Wednesday	7 minutes		

2 Jamila has her English book marked every day. One week her marks out of ten were as follows.

Monday	7	Thursday	6
Tuesday	4	Friday	9
Wednesday	9		

3 A small hotel serves lunches daily. One week the numbers served on each day were as follows.

Monday	33	Friday	36
Tuesday	37	Saturday	34
Wednesday	15	Sunday	31
Thursday	31		

4 One week a bricklayer worked on all seven days. The numbers of hours that he worked on each day were as follows.

Monday	10	Friday	9
Tuesday	9	Saturday	13
Wednesday	12	Sunday	9
Thursday	8		

5 Kerry's examination marks at the end of one term were as follows.

Mathematics	61	French	64
English	63	Science	70
History	40	Craft	68
Geography	61		

6 Mrs Jones buys a pack of tomatoes at a supermarket. The weights of each of the tomatoes in the pack are as follows.

72 g, 65 g, 70 g, 39 g, 71 g, 73 g and 65 g

7 At a fairground William has five shots with a rifle. The picture below shows his scores.

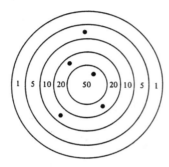

8 Anne throws a dice nine times and the scores are as follows.

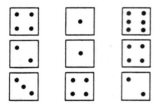

The range

The *range* of a group of values is found by subtracting the smallest value from the largest value.

Example 8

Find the range of

5, 6, 7, 5, 3, 3, 3, 5, 7, 8, 6,
2, 10, 5, 2, 7, 12, 9, 10, 5

Largest value = 12

Smallest value = 2

Range = 12 − 2 = 10

Exercise 8.7

Find the range of each group of values.

1 1, 2, 4, 8, 9, 4, 5, 7
2 23, 56, 29, 20, 19, 54, 53, 20
3 17, 17, 17, 18, 19, 20, 15, 29
4 0, 8, 9, 0, 2, 2, 3, 4, 5, 3, 6, 7, 2
5 100, 96, 95, 92, 93, 92, 91
6 62, 62, 62, 63, 65, 66, 66, 68, 66, 65, 65, 65
7 8, 8, 8, 8, 7, 7, 9, 9, 9, 6, 6, 6
8 50, 50, 50, 50, 50, 51, 51, 51, 51, 51, 51
9 0.5, 0.6, 0.7, 0.5, 0.6, 0.7, 0.8, 0.9, 0.5
10 0, 2, −2, 3, −4, 4, 3, −3, −2, 0, 4

A group of values or scores is called a *distribution*.

For example, Jake and Sally each take end of year exams in 10 subjects.

These are the *distributions* of their marks.

Jake's mark distribution
52, 64, 55, 61, 67, 5, 51, 60, 57, 62

Sally's mark distribution
85, 93, 72, 95, 23, 88, 17, 89, 92, 87

Two distributions can be compared using an average and the range.

Mean of Jake's marks = 58.4
Mean of Sally's marks = 74.1

Range of Jake's marks = 16
Range of Sally's marks = 78

We can compare the distributions and conclude that

(1) Sally's mean average mark is much higher than Jake's mean average mark. She has done better overall in the exams.

(2) The range of Jake's marks is much less than the range of Sally's marks. This shows that he is more consistent, doing roughly as well in all his subjects.
The range of Sally's marks show that she does very well in some subjects but very badly in others.

Example 9

These are the distributions of scores when two darts players each threw a set of three darts twelve times.

Eric's score distribution
98, 100, 100, 100, 100, 104,
105, 106, 120, 160, 160, 160

Jocky's score distribution
5, 5, 41, 60, 65, 66, 90,
100, 100, 180, 180, 180

a Find the median and range for each player's distribution.

b Compare the two distributions.

a Median of Eric's marks   = 104.5
Median of Jocky's marks = 78

Range of Eric's marks   = 62
Range of Jocky's marks = 175

b Eric has a higher median average score than Jocky, so on this evidence, he is a more accurate player.
Jocky did score three maximums (180 points) but the ranges of the distributions show that he is less consistent than Eric and his scores are much more widely spread.

Exercise 8.8

1 The contents of 20 boxes of Striko matches and 20 boxes of Katchwell matches are counted.

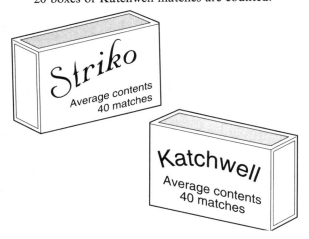

These are the distributions of number of matches per box.

Striko
37	38	38	38
39	39	40	40
40	40	40	40
41	41	41	41
42	42	43	44

Katchwell
35	36	36	37
38	38	39	39
40	40	40	40
40	41	43	45
45	47	48	51

a Find the mean and range for each distribution.

b Compare the two distributions.

2 Amarjit and Martha each fired 50 shots at a target.

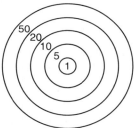

These are the distributions of their scores.

Amarjit
1	1	1	1	1
1	1	1	1	1
1	1	5	5	5
5	5	5	5	5
10	10	10	10	10
10	10	10	10	10
10	10	10	10	10
20	20	20	20	20
20	20	20	50	50
50	50	50	50	50

Martha
5	5	5	5	5
5	5	5	5	5
5	5	5	5	5
5	5	5	5	5
5	5	10	10	10
10	10	10	10	10
10	10	10	10	10
10	10	10	10	10
10	10	20	20	20
20	20	20	20	20

a Find the mean and range for each distribution.

b Compare the two distributions.

3 The captain of a cricket team is considering the distributions of batting scores for two of his players, Bill and Ted.

These are the distributions of their scores.

Bill	0	0	0	0	0
	1	3	29	33	42
	50	52	67	84	100
	101	120	147	153	184

Ted	0	27	35	42	44
	45	46	48	48	52
	58	62	66	71	74
	77	82	83	84	91

a Find the mean and range for each distribution.

b Compare the two distributions.

4 The cost in pence of one litre of petrol is checked at 50 garages in London and 50 garages in Newcastle.

These are the distributions of prices.

London	46.9	47.5	49.5	49.5	49.5
	49.5	49.5	49.9	49.9	50.9
	50.9	50.9	50.9	50.9	50.9
	52.9	52.9	52.9	52.9	52.9
	52.9	52.9	52.9	52.9	52.9
	52.9	52.9	52.9	52.9	52.9
	52.9	52.9	52.9	52.9	52.9
	52.9	52.9	52.9	52.9	52.9
	55.9	55.9	55.9	55.9	55.9
	55.9	55.9	57.9	59.9	59.9

Newcastle	47.9	47.9	47.9	48.9	48.9
	49.5	49.5	49.5	49.5	49.5
	49.5	49.5	49.9	49.9	49.9
	49.9	49.9	49.9	49.9	49.9
	49.9	49.9	49.9	49.9	49.9
	50.9	50.9	50.9	50.9	50.9
	50.9	50.9	50.9	50.9	50.9
	50.9	50.9	50.9	50.9	50.9
	51.9	51.9	51.9	51.9	51.9
	51.9	52.9	52.9	52.9	54.9

a Find the median and range for each distribution.

b Compare the two distributions.

5 Two ovens, the TooCool and the Burnall are being tested by a consumer magazine.
In one test, the ovens are set to 200 °C and the actual temperature inside the oven is measured every minute for one hour.

These are the distributions of actual temperatures.

TooCool	194	194	194	194	195
	195	195	195	195	195
	195	195	195	195	195
	196	196	196	196	196
	196	196	197	197	197
	197	197	197	197	197
	197	197	197	197	198
	198	198	198	198	198
	198	198	198	198	198
	198	198	198	198	198
	198	199	199	199	199
	199	199	199	199	199

Burnall	198	198	198	198	198
	198	198	198	198	198
	198	198	198	198	198
	199	199	199	199	199
	199	199	199	199	200
	200	200	200	200	200
	200	200	200	200	201
	201	201	202	202	202
	202	202	202	202	202
	202	202	203	203	203
	203	203	203	203	204
	205	205	206	207	208

a Find the median and range for each distribution.

b Compare the two distributions.